Diary of a Doctor

K. R. Krishnan

Thomas Giordani Wright, 1808-1898.

Photography had not yet been invented when Thomas was writing his Diary as a young man in the late 1820s. This photograph, the only one that is known to exist, shows him as a successful doctor in Wakefield, where he settled in 1833. It was probably taken during the 1850s.

Diary of a Doctor

Surgeon's Assistant in Newcastle

1826-1829

Thomas Giordani Wright

Extracts compiled and edited by
Alastair Johnson

Foreword by Roy Porter,
Professor of the Social History of Medicine,
Wellcome Institute for the History of Medicine, London

∾

Newcastle Libraries and Information Service
in association with Tyne & Wear Archives

Acknowledgements:

I thank first of all the members of the Nanaimo Historical Society, who recognised the significance of Thomas G. Wright's Diary after it was discovered in 1985 and made the manuscript accessible by donating it to the City of Newcastle upon Tyne.

I am also indebted to the staff of Tyne & Wear Archives whose resources and help made it possible for me to transcribe the Diary manuscript.

Newcastle Libraries & Information Service has played an important part in the production of this book. City Library supplied much of the background material and I thank particularly the staff of the Local Studies Section for helping me to unearth many details about life in early 19th century Newcastle. I also warmly thank Anna Flowers who not only found and arranged the illustrations but advised on the selection and presentation of the Diary extracts. I am grateful to Anthony Flowers for the design of the cover.

Alastair Johnson, 1998

The manuscript of Thomas G. Wright's Diary is held by Tyne & Wear Archives. A full transcript is to be published in 1999 by The Surtees Society (Hon. Sec. Mr A.J. Piper, 5 The College, Durham, DH1 3EQ).

Illustrations acknowledgements:

Illustrations are from collections in the Local Studies Section, Newcastle Libraries and Information Service, except for the following:

Frontispiece: Thomas Giordani Wright, courtesy of Pinderfields Hospital & West Yorkshire Archive Service;

Page 6: surgical instruments, courtesy of The Society of Antiquaries, Newcastle upon Tyne;

Pages 11, 14, 17, 41: instruments from A *System of Surgery*, B. Bell, 1801, courtesy of Wellcome Institute Library, London;

Front cover and pages 12, 96: Diary manuscript, courtesy of Tyne & Wear Archives;

Page 37: leech, reproduced from *A Treatise on the Medicinal Leech*, J.R. Johnson, 1816, courtesy of the Robinson Library, University of Newcastle upon Tyne;

Page 49: stethoscope, reproduced from *Treatise on the Diseases of the Chest*, R.T.H. Laennec, 1827, courtesy of the Robinson Library, University of Newcastle upon Tyne;

Page 85: Lit. & Phil. Library, courtesy of Literary & Philosophical Society, Newcastle upon Tyne.

Cover design by A.V. Flowers

Text of the Diary transcript and commentary © Alastair Johnson, 1998
Foreword © Roy Porter, 1998

Published by City of Newcastle upon Tyne
Education & Libraries Directorate
Newcastle Libraries & Information Service, 1998

ISBN 1 85795 014 3

Printed by Bailes the Printer, Houghton le Spring

Contents

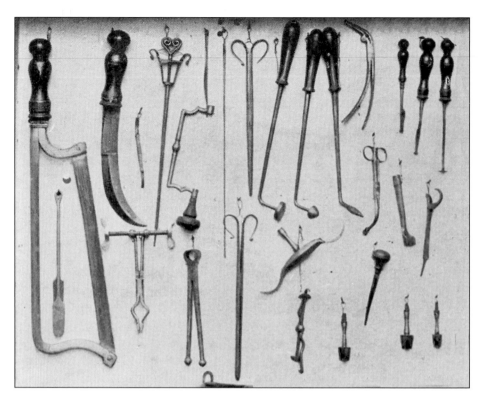

Tools of the trade.

Surgical instruments from the Barber Surgeons' Hall, Newcastle upon Tyne.

Foreword

MEMBERS OF THE OLDER generation tend to have rather warm memories of the trusted family doctor, an avuncular, tweed-jacketed, pipe-smoking Dr Finlay figure, on duty seven days a week, three-hundred and sixty-five days a year, and paying home calls at all hours. But our stereotypes of the medical men of earlier times are not so flattering.

We're used to caricatures of the ancestral surgeon as a Mr Sawbones, a brawny, butcher-like figure, armed with a far from clean lancet for letting blood and terrifying torture instruments for amputations – all done, before anaesthesia came in around 1850, with the poor patient conscious, if somewhat brandy befuddled. It doesn't surprise us when we find a Somerset parson cynically writing in his diary in 1802: 'Met Mr Forbes the surgeon going to kill a few patients'. Proverbial wisdom warned that death and the doctors were thick as thieves, or at least always conducted joint consultations. Practitioners, the joke ran, fleeced the public first and slew them afterwards. 'When a Nation abounds in Physicians,' bantered the *Spectator* magazine, early in the eighteenth century 'it grows thin of people'. 'If the world knew the villainy and knavery (beside ignorance) of the physicians and apothecaries', the gossipy antiquarian, John Aubrey, was told by a doctor, 'the people would throw stones at 'em as they walked in the streets'. Thomas Wright echoes these stereotypes when he records in his journal, 'the English surgeons are said to kill their patients, whilst the French ones let them die'. The old-style practitioner rarely got a good press.

Nor could his latter-day successor automatically be assured of a better reception. Tertius Lydgate is the spanking-new scientific doctor in George Eliot's novel *Middlemarch*, set in the 1830s. He has just returned, full of himself, from Paris, the powerhouse of the latest in medical education. To prove he's up-to-date, he's come armed with the latest Parisian medical fashion: the stethoscope. But to little avail, since most of the conservative clients in that sleepy Midlands town were to treat his novelties with the utmost suspicion. Deflating Lydgate's fantasy of himself as a new scientific community leader, a man whose expertise should command respect and compliance, George Eliot had Lady Chettam remark, 'For my own part, I like a medical man more on a footing with the servants'.

The image of the old-style medical practitioner was thus of a man frequently dangerous and generally despised. But as so often, fact differed from fiction. And one of the delights of Alastair Johnson's *Diary of a Doctor* lies in revealing how medicine was actually practised just before the fictional Dr Lydgate, and how the doctor was truly regarded by the community he served. Through the recently-discovered journals of Thomas Giordani Wright, assistant-surgeon, we get a rich and vivid depiction of medical practice in and around Newcastle in the 1820s.

We see, not surprisingly in view of the hazards of the local trades and industries, the incessant demand for the local doctor. Wright was constantly being called out to treat fractures and injuries caused by pit explosions or subsidences, and accidents in furnaces and workshops. He appears popular with the locals, not least because – as a young man without ties, beginning to make his way in the world – he seems more generous with his time, more ready to come out, than his master, the crusty McIntyre.

His relations with his patients, and their friends and families, were not all plain-sailing, however. Though they are always glad to see him, they are not afraid to tell him his business, what's wrong with them and what they need. And all too often, he feels he's been exploited, called out on some fool's errand. Woken up in the middle of the night by a messenger informing him a miner is almost dead, Wright struggles through the rain to find – it was all just a case of 'deep fright'; on other such cases, it's a trivial sprain or a minor cut! Yet there are often compensations for his efforts – for instance a 'capital cheese' which he was able to sample after seeing one of his patients.

Wright has mixed feelings about the largely labouring-class clientele whom he (as junior) gets to see. He sometimes portrays them as dirty and slovenly – housewives whose frying-pans have not seen a scourer for the last six months. But they are also cordial and striking in the kind of picturesque way which caught Thomas Bewick's eye. What Bewick did with his engravings, Wright does with his pen, offering little vignettes of stinking villages and cottage interiors, full of brawling brats, and affectionately transcribing their dialect speech.

What is so fascinating is that Wright, though but a humble assistant surgeon, not yet twenty when his journals commence, evidently had literary ambitions. Whilst his journal was meant to be read only by his close friends and relations, Wright was clearly writing for effect, obviously deriving pleasure from the moments snatched on Sundays to record the week's events, practising his skills with the pen no less than with the lancet. Mentioning his new 'steed', he dubs her a 'little frisky, fiery, fine-legged, fly away, foreign Flanders 5 year old filly'; in time we see him going beyond alliteration, growing in capacity to depict a scene or tell a tale.

As well as being the era of industrialisation and a time when medicine was in transition, it was also the age of Romanticism. Commonplace young fellows like Wright, who had grown up surrounded with news of heroes like Nelson and Napoleon, thought they had a little bit of the Byron in them, they wanted to cut a figure and establish their place in the world – and not least, as we see in due course with Wright, to impress the ladies.

Thomas Wright's journals offer a delightful picture of bygone Newcastle, vivid insights into pre-scientific medicine, and a window onto the mind and hopes of an ambitious provincial lad. It is a joy that they have been preserved and made available in this attractive selection.

Roy Porter
Professor of the Social History of Medicine, Wellcome Institute for the History of Medicine, London.

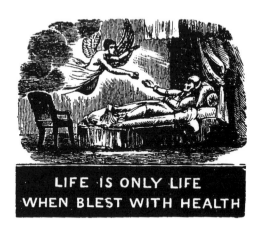

LIFE IS ONLY LIFE
WHEN BLEST WITH HEALTH

Introduction

IN MARCH 1824, shortly after his sixteenth birthday, Thomas Giordani Wright left his home near Darlington to start his training as a doctor by becoming an apprentice in Mr James McIntyre's 'extensive colliery practice' at Newcastle. Thomas soon settled into the work, helping in 'the shop', making up pills and potions, and visiting patients with his master. After he had been with Mr McIntyre about eighteen months, Thomas was delighted to be given the chance to take some medical courses in Edinburgh. When he had finished his studies and returned to his job in Newcastle in August 1826, he had new responsibilities. As well as having his 'own' patients to look after, he had to supervise the junior apprentices and do the accounts for the practice. Although all this meant a pretty busy life, it did not prevent Thomas making a start on a project he had been planning for some time. On October 1, 1826 he began his *Diary of a Doctor*. Amazingly, Thomas managed to keep his diary more or less up-to-date until he completed his apprenticeship and left Newcastle in May 1829. Even more amazingly, most of the manuscript has survived and has become available for us to read.

Thomas Wright's diary is a remarkable document, and there is hardly a page without something of interest. Naturally, Thomas wrote a lot about his work. His patients were mostly miners and their families. They lived in pit villages around Newcastle, and he often described his rounds – the long rides on horseback, the accidents and other cases he had to deal with, and the treatments he used. But Thomas did not want his diary to be just a repetitive description of his daily duties, and he did have lots of other things to write about. He was lively and curious, and got out and about whenever he could, to dances, the theatre, concerts, art exhibitions and the races. He played the flute, learned the quadrille, and played cards and partied with his friends.

Altogether Thomas Wright's diary gives a fascinating glimpse into what life was like in late Georgian Newcastle for a young man, with his life in front of him, at the outset of his career.

The history of the manuscript of *Diary of a Doctor* is interesting in itself. By the time he brought it to a close when he left Newcastle, Thomas had filled twelve of his home-made notebooks that he called 'volumes'. For more than 150 years, nothing was heard of the manuscript until, in 1985, nine of Thomas' original volumes turned up in a cardboard box found in the basement of a house in Nanaimo, a town on Vancouver Island in Canada. Fortunately, the old notebooks were given to the Nanaimo Historical Society, whose members took up the challenge of reading and transcribing the contents. They soon recognised that they were dealing with an important historical document of particular interest to the Tyneside region and, in 1990, they very generously sent the original volumes 'home' as a gift to the City of Newcastle, with the message:

> The Society though fascinated by the revelation of life in the English coal industry of the early 1800s, feel that nevertheless, these valuable records properly belong to the area where Dr Wright lived and worked. We return these Diaries to their source, happy in the knowledge that they will add greatly to your records and be a source of interest to physicians and historians alike.

These extracts are only a small part of Thomas Wright's diary, but I hope they give some idea of its style and content and convey some of the enthusiasm and zest for life of the author, a bright young man who lived in Newcastle so long ago.

Alastair Johnson, 1998

Case for caustic and red precipitate.

The Preface to Diary of a Doctor, written in 1834, is pasted into the first volume of the Diary manuscript.

Preface to Diary of a Doctor: To Eliza

Thomas Wright wrote this Preface about five years after he finished his Diary, when he gave it to his fiancée Eliza to read shortly before their marriage.

A word or two before you begin the perusal of this often talked of diary, my love! You will find it a very different sort of work from the Note Book you have been so much pleased with. This is by far less interesting. It is ill-written, ill-composed, and in many instances mis-spelled: but remember, dearest, it is my first attempt at scribbling, and that the rude pages you have now before you contain the effusions of a pen at eighteen whose writings you are very well satisfied with at six and twenty. If I had not practised in my Diary, my Note Book would never have been worthy of your smiles: be merciful, therefore in your criticisms. I know, love, I need say little on that score as you are already predisposed to be sufficiently partial, but really on looking over a few pages of this first number, it does seem so full of arrant nonsense that all your partiality will be requisite to make you think it worth reading. There will certainly be a little improvement in the future numbers, but a little is all I dare promise. I had not, when I scribbled their illegible pages, the inspiring emotions which now animate my pen, and give it a fluency (however little merit it has else) that it never before possessed.

In the Diary you will find much that was not intended for publication beyond my immediate friends; and much that would not have been inserted in a book that was solely for lady's perusal. My Diary, however, at the time, was my Case-Book professionally as well as non-professionally; and in its details there is, of course, much that is unintelligible to you. All that you can skip over; as you proceed you will come at many passages that will be more interesting.

In order that you may understand the dramatis personae of the narrative, I must premise, that at the time the Diary opens Mr McIntyre's establishment consisted of the following persons. McI himself then residing in Newgate Street Newcastle: a low-bred Scotchman Mr Cochrane, who yet remains his assistant in the Backworth district, and who had just gone to reside at a house Mr McI had taken for him near Backworth; he attended the practice connected with five collieries in his neighborhood: next myself, living with Mr McI and having charge of six collieries around NCastle and the inferior practice of the house; Mr King an ill-educated lad who was indentured to Mr McI about the same time I was, and who was about to take his turn of a winter's session at Edinburgh, – a simple but good-natured fool: and two junior apprentices who were both reprobates and whose fate was at length equal to their deserts; – one after being turned away three times was finally dismissed with a conviction of theft added to all his other misdemeanours, and the other after being indulged beyond measure, and only threatened when he should have been punished became so debauched that he attempted to poison himself in a drunken fit, and was twice turned away – the last time peremptorily so.

With these rebellious spirits as my subs, and a reserved proud and selfish Scotchman as my Governor (though he has done much to make up for what I then thought unjust treatment, since I left him) my Eliza may now contemplate me, six weeks after my return to Mr McI from Edinburgh and assuming my place as his Assistant, entering upon the details of the 'Diary of a Doctor'.

May 13 1834

'Men should know why
They write and for what end, but note or text
I never know the word which will come next.
So on I ramble, now and then narrating,
Now pondering ...'

Thomas wrote this quotation, from Byron's 'Don Juan', as a motto at the beginning of each volume of his Diary.

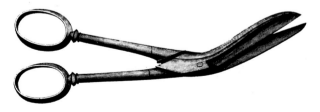

Crooked scissors.

What is to be the plan of this said diary?

On the first day of his Diary, October 1 1826, Thomas wrote about his hopes for it before getting down to business, describing his new horse and some of his patients.

Is it to be professional, historical or common place? It is to be all; to contain remarks professional & remarks nonprofessional; comic & sentimental; spiritual & temporal; military & civil; it is to receive observations on the wind & on the weather; observations literary; scientific, & philosophical; it is to contain superscriptions, subscriptions, inscriptions & prescriptions; prognoses diagnoses and all the rest of the family of noses; remarks pathological, physiological, osteological and all the other compounds of logical; in short it will be as varied in its pages as its authors life & thoughts, dull or lively as his humour prompts, and leave existence for a day, or swell that day 'thro leaves unnumbered' as leisure or inclination permits; or finally in all probability be brought to a premature end …

I have got a new steed to ride my daily rounds on, – a little frisky, fiery fine-legged, fly away, foreign Flanders 5-yr old filly, – which so far, (I have gone two journeys on her) I like exceedingly. She seems unaccustomed to the country, which is rather a startling one to most horses at first. Mr Cochrane is to ride her as soon as the grey highland mare, at present out at grass, returns; i.e. if he can. This little mare was the first 'beast' I fell off, as yesterday I unfortunately lost my balance in looking at her feet, while only walking, and was 'spilt'. No detriment to my equestrian skill tho': be it known to all whom it concerneth.

I have two or three severe accidents under my care just now; they are as follows:

Ritson, Benwell High Cross.

A severe cut upon the front of the tibia, extending more or less from the patella downward. A little above the ancle the bone was laid quite bare for about $\frac{1}{2}$ inches. A great deal of coal dust & dirt were fixed into the wound, which I have removed by poultices; and the wounds are now dressed … He got his accident by a stone falling upon him on the 20th of Septr.

Newcastle upon Tyne from the south in 1827.

A busy, growing town with a population of about 40,000, Newcastle was the business and commercial centre for Tyneside. As a port it ranked in the country second only to London, shipping most of the coal used by the capital city as well as chemicals, soap and glass produced by the factories along the River Tyne. By the 1820s, many of the prosperous residents, those who had done well out of industrialisation, lived in better-class houses outside the old town walls. Most of the town's population still lived in squalid, crowded, slums on the banks of the river.

Grantson, Elswick New Row.

An accident in every respect like the above but not quite so severe. It happened Septr: 28th. The lad is applying Poultices still.

Gascoigne, Heaton High Pit.

The Index of the right hand was hanging by the skin off by the second phalanx. The middle finger is quite off by the third phalanx. The index of the left hand is split down in the end, and the integument of that middle finger totally detached & torn. I have endeavoured to unite the right index by the first intention, after removing the bone … Poultices are applying & yesterday I opened out the plaster, but I am afraid it will come off …

Thornton, Wallsend Shiney Row.

A terrible compd fractured leg. He has had it nearly a month, and it is now healing, but the sinuses and abscesses are very numerous. As Mr McI is oftener down that way, he attends principally to this case tho' I often dress the patient. I was there with Mr McI this morning.

There are numerous other cases of minor importance, but which may perhaps require to be mentioned hereafter. This is Sunday, or I should never have been able to have written this long rigmarole for a commencement. I must now however leave off for tonight.

Saw for amputating arms and legs.

October 7, 1826

Thomas was often too busy to write his Diary every day, but brought the reader up to date when he did have time. Most of our Diary extracts are just part of one day's entry, but this full day gives some idea of his busy life.

Called out this morning to a man burnt at Elswick. Not very severe. Mare goes quite well again, or nearly so.

A cast of a tumour sent home this morning for which the mould was made last Saturday. The dimensions are Extreme length ft 2 3 in Breadth ft 1 10 in & greatest circumference ft 4 4 in. It is situated on a woman's right shoulder & back, and is supposed to weigh about 2 stones.

By the bye a large abscess formed in Gascoigne's hand, which Mr McI opened yesterday.

Called down at 4 PM to a lad at Walker, who was 'bleeding to deead'. He had got a cut on the head about a week ago, in which, I presume, some branch of the temporal artery had been partially cut thro; and which had ulcerated the coats, and so caused the accident. The boy (about 12 years old) was very weak & excessively pale when I got down to him, but the haemorrhage was stopped. I probed the wound, but as no bleeding returned, I judged it better to apply a compress and bandage than to search for the open vessel. Got a cup of tea with patient's mother Mrs Shields; I drank tea with Mrs Jennant, Benwell, yesterday too.

On calling upon a patient at Johnson's Houses I encountered a large cheese and a spirit bottle set out upon the table. The dame having been 'brought to bed' on Thursday. A capital cheese it was.

Made a call upon Mrs Scott, Castle Street. Mr McIntyre had tried Acid Nitros c Opio in Mist. Camph. [*a mixture of nitric acid, opium and camphor*] … without effect in stopping a violent cholera. She was complaining of excruciating pain in the head when I saw her in the morning, and vomited all her medicine … I gave her one of her pills, and after it Tr Opii [*tincture of opium*] in a small quantity of water, which remained upon her stomach and gave her ease in ten minutes. Mr McI came in whilst I was yet there in the morning, and ordered me to see her this evening. When I called she was a great better. 'Believes if I had not seen her she would have died', 'wonders Mr McI never gave her those drops', as this is the second time I have relieved her in the same way … Mrs S. both received & dismissed me with many a blessing. People talk of the vexations of a surgeon's life, this is one example of the contrary.

Called upon Mr Church to request him to go with me to Wallsend tomorrow. I wished to persuade him to take the gig, (the real reason was I had no clean breeches to put on, & I make a rule never to ride in my dress black trowsers) but he will not, and wishes to have my mare, fearing he says that 'the black horse, being a foreigner, may have learned some foreign manners'.

The 'cholera' referred to here was not the violent, and often lethal, epidemic disease that first struck Tyneside in 1831. At the time of the Diary, the term 'cholera' was often used for illnesses where there was violent vomiting and diarrhoea.

CHOLERA MORBUS.

THE Cholera Morbus is a violent purging and vomiting, attended with gripes, sickness, and a constant desire to go to stool. It comes on suddenly, and is occasioned by the putrid acrimony of the bile, or food that turns sour on the stomach; and feels like the symptoms of the heart-burn or cardialgia, with flatulence, and pain in the stomach and bowels.

At the beginning of this disease, the offending cause may be assisted by promoting a purge or emetic. It depends on your knowledge, when you see the patient, what treatment to use.

R.   Tincture opium   -   - gutt. xl
     Aqua menth. pip, or mint-waters   - ℥ j
            Fiat haust. statim.
Two hours after repeat the same haust. occasionally.

From the popular self-help medical manual: 'Every Man His own Doctor', by William Henderson, published in Newcastle upon Tyne, 1827.

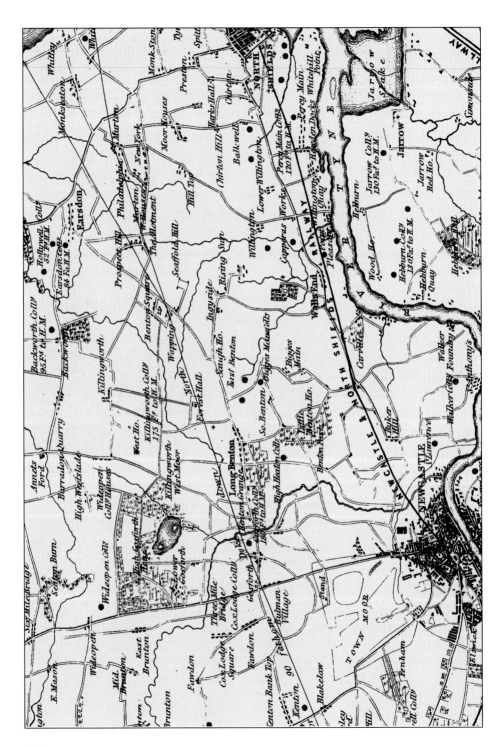

The job – patients and colleagues

What was it like, being assistant to Mr James McIntyre? Thomas tried hard to become a good doctor, but there were often frustrating difficulties with transport, unreasonable patients, unreliable colleagues and with Mr McIntyre himself. He could be a hard task-master and Thomas did not always see eye-to-eye with him.

Getting in among my patients

Because of transport problems patients in Byker had not been visited as often as they should. Some of them came to the surgery in Newcastle to complain.

I have been very much put out of my element by my mare taking ill of a severe cold; and my consequently not getting so much among my patients. I have had to walk myself, or send my junior Greenwood to dress Brabant every day, and have only got twice down the Shields Road these ten days. I went with Mr McI in the gig. Mr McI's horse was knocked up too, so we had to get a hack for the vehicle even. We were in both instances behind times and in a great hurry to the great annoyance, and astonishment of our Byker Hill patients. Our last visit of the kind was Sunday se'enight, and unless a call at the door from Mr McI in passing, these Byker Hill folk (Byker Hill being the focus of Heaton Colliery & a great depot of our 'sick') had never been seen from then to the following Saturday. On Saturday three or four of them (i.e. the patient's friends) came in almost together. I stood over the fire, with my coat-laps toward it, the wives sat around, while the husbands were talking at the door. The women began to attack Mr McI's bustling attentions pretty sharply, while I defended him as well as I could, poor man! They 'sure'd Mr McI needn't be

The map (left) shows Newcastle in 1838, several years after Thomas left the practice. By this time the new railways to the coast, to Carlisle and south of the Tyne had been constructed, and they doubtless would have made Thomas's life a little easier. However, the road system had not changed much since Thomas's stay in Newcastle, and we can see what long distances he had to cover on horseback. Benwell Colliery is at the extreme left of the map while Backworth, Mr McIntyre's far flung outpost, is about seven miles north-east of Newcastle, at the top of the map.

in sich a hurry in coming to see them, or to think he did them a favour by coming to see them himself, for they did na want to see him'. They liked me to go a deal better; and 'as long as Mr McI had sich nice foremen as the last three or four, he might keep away as lang as he liked; without it was a case of particular necessity, like; then he ought undoubtedly to knaw better, but still even then some people put as much confidence in Mr Gibson, when he was there, as himself' … These folk on Saturday too told me that if I got as good a word every where as I did at Byker Hill, and about there, I would do (as Mrs Wilkinson said also of my sticking plaster.) My Benwell patient's mother told me the other day too, that if all my patients 'made sae mich wark about me coming to see them mysel as her son did' she 'did na knaw how I would get through them all'. So much for my getting in among my patients. All this is very pleasant to me.

I ordered him a mutton chop

Changing the prescribed treatment was sometimes successful.

A patient is considerably better today, indeed almost well again. I at first considered his complaint as Dyspepsia, and accordingly kept him low (he had some fever) gave him purges &c with a little tonic medicine after them. He got no better; and gave me a long history of his being often affected with this complaint when his complaints ended in nervous fever &c &c. I, having read a little while ago a paper in the Medico chirurgical review (I think it was) on Gastralgia conjectured it might very probably be a case of that disease, and reversed my plan of treatment. I ordered him a mutton chop and a glass of

On the outskirts of Newcastle.

brandy and water daily, along with some more powerful tonic powders. This has been followed by the best effects, he has been better ever since he took the powders on Sunday, and says he is now better than before I took him through Lands. His wife says 'he cracks sair o' them last poothers he got'. He is the more pleased as he expected another 'seven weeks bout'.

A ride in the country

Thomas here describes a typical round of patients on his horse. He left Newcastle via the Quayside, and made his way to the Shields road – the turnpike from Newcastle to North Shields – and on to Heaton.

Passing the Keelman's Hospital and the Royal Jubilee school we come upon the veritable Shields road which barring and excepting a preterparticularly considerable thick eight-inch covering of mud in winter, and an impenetrable cloud of stour in Summer, is a very delightful piece of turnpike. Here then we go a jog trot to Ouseburn a sort of outskirt Village where your every faculty is put in instant requisition. After crossing the bridge your nose is assailed by a combination of all the odours that can render smell disagreeable, and till your taste shares the sensation. A steam mill and iron foundry vapour on the one hand and lime kilns on the other, with a tripe shop in the van and a general receptacle for manure at the rear, all lend their aid toward this delectable perfume. Nor do your ears enjoy a greater repose; the combined powers of a dozen or two of hammers upon the melodious tones of a steam engine boilers from three forges in close contiguity afford a delicious & harmonious treat while the unchapelled, crowded burial ground, backed and shaded by a well-controlled pit heap rising like a mountain in the distance and flanked by a high row of houses with not the most seemly habiliments hanging from the anything-but glazed windows, present a picture equally agreeable to the eye.

Bridge over the Ouseburn.

… The Heaton domain extends … about 2 miles north, 1 east and half a mile south; and upon it are two pits in full work and three at present unemployed. The pitmens' houses are generally built in long rows of two houses in breadth each containing one room a garret and a pantry. The overmen and those who have large families or who are favorites may obtain two rooms, perhaps three, as some of the houses are so built for the purpose. These are furnished according to the disposition or means of the occupier but one thing is uniformly good – the fire.

Coals, lodgings and flannel dresses are supplied by the Colliery owners and the additional wages amount from 15/- to 20/- a week per man. (The coal trade is now so bad that 20/- per fortnight is often all a man can make being only allowed to work 3 or 4 days a week.) In many instances large masses of high built houses are rented by the colliery and separate rooms portioned out to each family. Every householder is provided with a small garden and generally keeps a pig or two, fat bacon being a favourite dish.

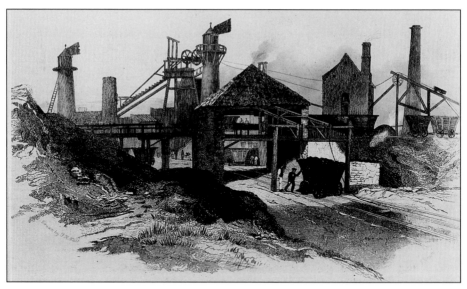

Church Pit Wallsend c.1841 (by T.H. Hair).

Wallsend colliery's first shaft, to the High Main seam at a depth of 666 feet, was completed in 1781. After that seam had been largely worked-out, the new Bensham seam, 204 feet lower down, was opened in 1821 using some of the old shafts. The coal here was of poorer quality, and more difficult and dangerous to mine because of the presence of large quantities of explosive gas.

Leaving Byker Hill and arriving at the 2 mile stone we come at Smasher's Row which may be set down as the commencement of Walker Colliery. This concern is as large (but not so respectable) as Heaton having 3 pits at present working. It includes Biggs Main, Battle Hill and other masses of Houses ... Wallsend contains more workmen and a greater extent of territory than any of the rest of our collieries and yet little business is carried on in the doctoring way there. The work is very bad just now at this concern and men are employed to do all the work by way of bettering their wages the horses having been sold about a month since.

Turning my horse's head about at the Church Pit Wallsend, – my utmost limit and a little beyond the fourth mile stone – I continue my route through Biggs Main – past the Red & White Halls, Benton farm, Heaton High Pit – Jesmond Bridge – Lambert's Leap and Sandyford stone. I return into Newcastle at the opposite end to that by which I left it viz. the Barras Bridge, having seen in my tour on a moderate calculation about a score of patients and with my brain full of prescriptions ready for delivery into the day book.

Barras Bridge, now beneath the city centre, had a rural air in the early 19th century.

A house in Heaton

Thomas described one of his more unpleasant house calls.

... I came to Johnson's houses, a mass belonging to Heaton, where I have to dress a boy who has long been under care with an abscess in his knee. On entering the door not without many qualms and sundry hints from the nose to the stomach, one would suppose a family of  negroes and copper colored indians were mingled. Those of the batch who had just returned from the pit were of the former color while the rest having the 'thick scraped off' presented the latter appearance ... Dinner is on the table. The frying pan unsullied by dish-clout for the last six months stands on the fire sending forth the savory fumes of a few fat slices of bacon. A dish of half-boiled potatoes is under the bars and a half dozen of broken plates, dirty spoons and one-pronged forks strewed about the chairs and table, if the furniture be worthy of that title. A mess of cabbage leaves and hot water with some bread in it serves the bairns for broth and washing their fingers in. The salves &c are brought out for my use without at all disarranging the dinner set out, the steaming poultices laid on one of the plates; – but I dare not finish the picture; suffice it I completed my operations as quickly as possible and from this amalgamation of salve, soup, salt butter, plaster, pancakes & poultices I made a bolt and mounting my horse rode off ...

Thomas was very careful, after writing this, to make it clear that it was not at all typical of his miner patients, most of them being very respectable, with neat, spotless homes.

Called out of my bed

The doctors were not called out at night too often – no telephones in those days! But sometimes Thomas was called out unnecessarily. For example in October 1826:

I was, for the first time since I became assistant, called out of my bed to an accident. The people sent off in a great hurry, thinking the lad (at Biggs Main) was nearly killed, but on mature & deliberate consideration, which took place before I got down, he was adjudged to be mistaken, and very little worse; accordingly put to bed, the doors closed, and all made quiet, so that when I got to the house, I had the family (patient & all) to waken from their beds & a sound sleep. I met the usual consolation upon such occasions, (after a cold ride for nothing at 5 in the morning, and the lad just a bit cut on the leg which he said he could 'haeve dressed weel aneugh hissel') – 'Oh! aw's sure its weel its nae warse, its a marcy he wasna killed outright', together with a twentieth edition of a full & particular account of his miraculous escape &c &c.

The night was very rainy

Another thoughtless patient had to be seen in May 1827.

Many a week has passed since I have been treated with a 'ride in the country' by night; but at midnight's fearful hour, or rather just after the clock struck one this morning, I received a summons to see a man at Wallsend belonging to Walker colliery.

The night was very rainy but armed against the weather by a stout great coat and old hat I set out for my place of destination. On the road I learned from

the messenger that though the good man had happened his accident before 10 PM he was so very considerate i.e. had taken such a length of time for mature deliberation as to the exact nature of his injury, that the doctor was not sent for till three hours had elapsed and I had fallen into a sound, sound sleep. Before I reached the house the patient had further considered that he might as well take a nap till the doctor came. Accordingly, himself, the wife and the family were with difficulty roused from their slumbers. Upon discovering the true state of the case, I found that my patient had received a severe, deep-seated fright, but had fortunately sustained no other injury except a slight bruise on the ancle. In consequence I had no further trouble than merely remounting my horse and riding back the same four miles I had already come in the same soaking incessant rain, and with the pleasant addition of being so completely wet through my great coat that I had even to wring the sleeves of my shirt on getting home. 'Oh! the pleasures of a ride in the Country'.

Mr McI has been putting upon me …

Thomas usually enjoyed his work with patients, but hated the accounts he had to do over Christmas and New Year.

I never was in a more disagreeable humour (to myself) that I have been in for this last week … Greenwood has got leave to go home for three days leaving me to do all the business … Mr McI too has been putting upon me rather more than I thought consistent with my office and has found fault too with me for Greenwood's negligence & tho' only three or four words it is more than I like by any means, when I have worked so hard lately for him in the account way, having got them done much sooner than usual. And yet too he comes in – 'Have you got them all made out?' 'Where is the list of them?' 'You should have had the ledger posted up' &c &c before the year was up. If he had them to do himself he would find talking and doing are here different matters.

I have almost begun lately to adopt J. Gibsons opinion that the more a person does for Mr McI the more they may do. He seems to act upon that plan a good deal thinking, no doubt – 'Yes now Wright seems to work very hard and very cheerfully at it too. I think I had better give him plenty to do now that I have got one that will do it without grumbling'. He has even requested me to carry out any of the accounts that lay in my rides and I see is planning rounds for me in every direction for that purpose when no patients require seeing. But I might continue on with this treasonable train for ever and a day and must try to find some more agreeable subject. I will keep steady to my duty and Mr McI will in the end find his mistake in the insubordination and consequent disorder he is creating in the surgery, by lowering my office.

A most laughable anecdote

Thomas had a pretty low opinion of his junior colleagues, the other apprentices, thinking them ill-educated and boorish. Sometimes patients told him tales that confirmed his own opinion.

… In being out at Benwell Old Engine the other day, I met with an old patient who I often used to dress when he had a very severe compd fractured leg at Benwell High Cross. He was telling me a most laughable anecdote of 'that grand swaggerin' chap & t'Hexham lad' coming out to persuade a man that his arm was broken, and tying it up 'wi their pasteboards & spelks' accordingly; whereas on Mr McI's seeing it the following day, it proved to be only a sprain!! My informant's own dry way of telling the story, added to the idea of the scene, was as good as a farce. Mr King often used to tell me of the many fractures he and Mr Bewicke had reduced; and which had all done so well!! This and a collar bone are the only two fractures I can hear of their having attempted to reduce.

The 'grand swaggerin' chap & t'Hexham lad' were Thomas's fellow apprentices, Bewicke and King. 'Spelks', a Tyneside word for wood splinters, probably means a wooden splint used for the supposed fracture.

Benwell High Cross

A shower came on

Mr McIntyre usually comes over as remote and distant, but occasionally a warmer side appears.

A ludicrous scene occurred this morning. I followed Mr McI down and as the morning was fine, did not (after his example) put on my 'upper Benjamin' . By the time I got to the High Cross however, a shower came on and I was glad to borrow a coat or jacket such as I could get of a man there. I left it & my horse at Benwell Stables, when I met Mr McI, and we walked down to Paradise Row where the man lives. It was raining hard when we got back to the Stables, and Mr McI asked Ritchie (a very stout man and horsekeeper) for the loan of his great coat. Ritchie produced it. It hung about Mr McI like 'Will Waddles' skin in Colman's story. He asked at first for a straw rope to put about it to complete his dress but finally got a strap buckled round him. When I put on the one I had brought down, which was the counterpart of the one Mr McI had on, and had been in the owners possession (he said) about 20 years, we formed a most ridiculous set, out to ride to Newcastle, and set to work to laugh at one another. The rain going off by the time we got back to the High Cross again, we 'doffed' our outer costumes and left them there.

I have it macerating

Mr McIntyre and his assistant were keen to improve their knowledge by carrying out post-mortem examinations. Often, the dead person's relatives refused permission but, in January 1827, the doctors got the chance to examine an interesting case.

Mr McI & I alone were there. When I was sowing up the parts again, Mr McI said to some of the friends 'It will soon be just as it was again'. My thoughts added 'minus his gall bladder – poor man' ! I have it macerating and expect it will make a fine morbid preparation of which I will give a description when I have got the dissection completed. A great deal of juggling we had to get it snugly pocketed for of course there were some men in the room.

Thomas didn't get round to examining the stolen gall bladder until about two months later.

 … here I will give a description of the Gall Bladder which I took from a defunct patient at Walker … his said viscus is now in a jar properly strung up.

It is immensely thickened and the Cystic duct would no doubt be almost or entirely obliterated. Mr McI said to me on taking it out of the intestines 'I think the duct is quite closed, – I do not see any vestige of it'. No wonder he could see no vestige when he had left that, the most important part – in the body! When I came to examine the specimen minutely at home, I found Mr McI had cut away the neck of the bladder just at the giving off of the duct.

Sometimes complete humbug

The English surgeons are said to kill their patients, whilst the French ones let them die. Now Mr McI, being as aforementioned a Scotchman, and that nation from long ancient intercourse with the French having picked up a number of their notions, has apparently acquired an affinity to them in this respect also. Certainly as a physician his treatment is far from bold, approaching sometimes to complete humbug.

DR JAMES'S POWDER.

THIS celebrated Medicine is invariably adopted by Physicians; and for those who cannot obtain Medical Advice, with each Packet, are enclosed full Directions for its Use. Its Efficacy is most certain if freely given on the attack of Fever, Measles, Sore Throat, recent Cold with Cough, and other Inflammatory Disorders. In Rheumatism and Chronic Complaints it has performed the most extraordinary Cures, when used with Perseverance. Dr James's Powder continues to be prepared by Messrs NEWBERY, from the *only Copy* of the Process left by Dr James in his own Hand Writing, which was deposited with their Grandfather in 1746, as Joint Proprietor. In Packets 2s. 9d. & 24s.

Dr JAMES's ANALEPTIC PILLS afford constant Relief in Indigestion, Bilious and Stomach Complaints, Gouty Symptoms, recent Rheumatism, and Cold with slight Fever, and are so mild in their Effects as not to require confinement. Dr James's Analeptic Pills are prepared by Messrs NEWBERY from *the only Recipe existing under Dr James's Hand*, and are sold by them in Boxes at 4s. 6d. each, at 45, St Paul's Church Yard; and their Agents in most Country Towns. The Name "*F. Newbery*" is engraved on each Government Stamp.

From the Newcastle Courant, June 24 1826.

Three doctors were arrived

A man came in this morning from Walker with a long tale that 'a person at Biggs Main had got his foot nearly taken off'. Accordingly the horse was ordered into the gig though at 4AM – and the amputating case &c &c put ready. To give every advantage to Greenwood, Mr McI took him up at the town end, and we all three proceeded down to the place. As I fully expected, the hurt was slight. The man had a cut upon his foot the size of my finger nail!! To dress which (he might have done it well enough himself) three doctors were arrived! In coming up again about half past 5, I sung in thought the following stanzas.

Air 'When first I came to London Town'

Behold! Three doctors coming now,
In a gig, Sir, In a gig, Sir,
Here's three doctors coming now,
For to see a patient!

Oh! Sir, ye might have spaed yor horse
(Nay dinna now begin to curse)
It's well, an sure 'at its nae warse!
Don't ye think sae now ye're here Sir!

We were sairly fraid, there was summat wrong
About his anklet; 'bout his anklet,
His banes ye see's not verra strang
He's but a smally lad, Sir

A coal fell frae the roof, ye ken;
It struck upon his knee; and then,
It shived right down by his shin bane;
What a wonder it's not broken!

When we sent away, – it teuk five men,
Indeed it did; indeed it did, Sir!
It teuk four putters & wor Ben
To lift him out o' danger

To get the coal frae of his foot,
And into 't cairt to get him put,
We expected nought but it was cut,
It's a marcy he's not killed, Sir.

I would plan this way

In July 1828, nearly two years after starting his Diary, Thomas spent some time, in charge, at the surgery at Backworth when Mr Cochrane was away. There, he had time to think about how the practice was run. This extract gives a glimpse of the Backworth area at that time.

It is a question which has often been put to me, and may readily be asked by the reader, how I should like to fill the situation of assistant at this department of Mr McIntyre's practice. One of my predecessors at Newcastle (Mr Rhodes) lately asserted he would not remain here for £500 a year. This would enable me to keep such a genteel house as to draw my friends around me in the lone winter months; and to take a standing in the first society of the district. At such a salary, I would become stationary here, for a few years, but not for much less. It would require a handsome remuneration to make up for the total want of company which this dreary spot presents …

Annoyed by the incessant rattle & din of a colliery incline both before and behind it – the surgeon's house faces the north-east, and stands in the midst of a group of pitman's cottages flanked by a little shop (Mr Cochrane's sister who kept his house married the owner of this shop. The brother & her have not spoken since) and the Northumberland Arms public house. The cold damp

The Northumberland village of Backworth c.1890.

east & North Easters are so well known on this coast as hardly to require mention here. They blow upon average one half the year, I dare say; and beat upon this exposed situation with a bitter effect.

Sitting as I am while writing this at Mr Cochrane's bedroom window, the wind having got into the wsw and the sky clear & fine, the look out is pleasant enough. The stone farmhouse prettily covered with green – a dry bridge crossing the rail road, and the smoky but new stone engine house – form the foreground …

… Instead of the present residence and establishment of Mr McIntyre's representative here, were I as full of practice and as big a gentleman as him, I would plan this way. On some pleasant green slope to the south of Earsden (or on any other spot that was cheap & convenient) I would buy, lease or rent an acre or two of land and on it build a neat genteel snug little country box with pleasant gardens, stables, surgery &c. With a paddock and a piece of kitchen garden this would require a trifling annual expenditure. A man & woman servant (some steady body say & his wife) might keep it in order. Two assistants should be procured – one might suffice if I did not run off to Edinburgh, and all over the country very often; – members of the College and with genteel salaries perhaps £100 a year with board & lodging in the family. One of these gentlemen to reside in the country and one at Newcastle. Three apprentices divided between the two places would be sufficiency. The 'commander in chief' to spend his time at one or other domicile as suited his pleasure or inclination; each being fitted to receive him or even a wife and family if necessary, in the summer season. The increase in practice which would follow such a step would amply repay the little extra expenditure; though an annual income amounting nearly to thousands ought to support an establishment which would then be decidedly the first surgical practice in the North!

By 'members of the College', Thomas meant qualified doctors. At that time the minimum qualification to practise medicine legally was a License from the Society of Apothecaries. However many ambitious practitioners also became Members of the Royal College of Surgeons by taking examinations in surgery.

The job – accidents

Benwell pit had fired

'An accident took place in the high part of Benwell Colliery near Newcastle by which two young men, named Joseph Whitfield and William Peel, were killed instantly. Several men were injured. There were upwards of 100 men and boys in the mine at the time. The cause assigned for this explosion was, that Peel went with a candle into a part of the mine where he and the rest had been cautioned not to go.' (Sykes, 'Local Records' 27 October 1826)

This day will be an eventful era in the annals of many a family … an express came to say that the 'Benwell Pit had fired', and he had scarcely got his message delivered, before he was followed by another man on the same errand. Luckily Mr McI was in, and 'to horse and away' was the immediate order. The first person I saw was a lad with his thigh broke & which I left, while getting washed, to attend to a man severely burnt all over at Paradise Row. He I hope will recover. Just as we were leaving him, the cart brought home one of the remaining two, who were till then missing dreadfully burnt, and tho' he was properly dressed I doubt he will not survive long. The lad we first saw was then dressed. His right thigh was fractured, and that leg very much cut, his right clavicle started from its articulation at its sternal end. About 5 of the front teeth in the upper jaw completely knocked out; three of those in the lower jaw broken quite inwards, the lips cut, & the face all scratched & cut with the coals

An underground scene from 'A Treatise on the Winning and Working of Collieries', by Matthias Dunn, Newcastle upon Tyne, 1848.

he had fallen (or rather been shot) amongst. The leg was dressed; the fracture reduced, then the dislocation of the clavicle, and lastly the teeth put right. The extremities were at first very cold, but by warm bricks &c a more general warmth pervaded when we left him. Greenwood, from not returning, has, I suppose, (6 PM) been left to look to the burnt men. Several accounts have been in; the last just now says the man so dreadfully burnt is living yet.

A lad is crushed at Elswick

In November 1827, Thomas attended a boy at Elswick, who had been crushed between two corves – big wickerwork baskets used down the mine to move the coal. He gave the usual treatment – bleeding and purging – but, two days later, Thomas was called out again.

They sent in last night to say the lad at Elswick was much the same. An injection had been given, but with no effect, and nothing would remain on his stomach. The leeches had bled well. I ordered the warm bath, and 'I would see him in the morning'. The father was in first thing this morning to say he was no better, his bowels swelled, and very painful, but he had taken a drink of coffee and some biscuit without vomiting. I went up to consult Mr McI, and he

From 'Views of the Collieries in Northumberland and Durham', by T.H. Hair, 1844. A crane loads rollies (wagons) with corves (baskets).

gave his opinion as follows, (I had previously ordered a blister & some Croton oil pills to be got ready). 'You had better give him some leeches & a blister afterward.' 'He has had a dozen leeches, sir, and a blister is preparing.' 'They must use injections'. 'He has had some, sir, but without effect'. 'Give him some Croton oil pills then, you know you must get his bowels open; and some purging mixture'. 'The pills are ready, I believe, sir'. Accordingly I went out to see him but on the road met a messenger to say he was dead. Most probably a rupture of some of the viscera caused death.

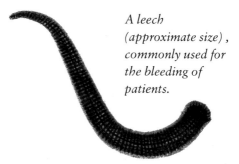

A leech (approximate size), commonly used for the bleeding of patients.

Head cut at Heaton High Pit

Thomas describes the treatment of wounds at a time before bacteria, antiseptics and anaesthetics were known about.

… about six o'clock the Heaton messenger came in – a lad had got his head cut at Heaton High Pit. I went out in quick time and a terrible cut it was. A part of the Scalp the size of my whole hand at least was completely detached in a flap … After a deal of pains & trouble I got the hair cut off, then shaved the head all round the flap and the flap itself clean. I washed the parts well and removed all the hair, dirt &c in the wound. A vessel bled violently, a branch of the occipital artery; so I drew a ligature around it and having brought the surfaces into as close apposition and inserted two sutures I applied adhesive plaster strips, a pledget, compress & bandage. My patient was easy when I left him and inclined to sleep, but roused himself a little to sing out for something to eat! I had given him 25 drops of tincture of opium before dressing.

Boy falls from Benwell Staith

... The boy who fell from Benwell Staith is very much bruised. I bled him today. His fall was 21 feet. He had had concussion of the brain which Mr. McI did not mention to me and said, when I went out on Sunday, 'if his pulse is quick you had better take a little blood from him.' His pulse was 100 & very weak. I did not therefore bleed him either then or yesterday. His pulse yesterday 98 still weak. In speaking of him to me Mr McI said I 'ought to have bled him' as the weak pulse was from 'concussion of the brain'. If he had only told me that there had been concussion I certainly know very well that a weak pulse indicates bleeding. Today I did bleed him however. He is doing pretty well after brisk leeching & purging.

A drawing of a coal staith (1848) showing the pivoting operation of lowering coal brought from local mines into small boats or 'keels'.

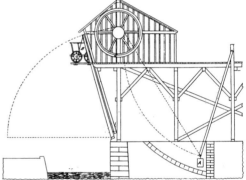

Struck by a stone

I was ... called up to an accident – and a terrible accident it was. A man had got struck by a stone falling from the roof of the pit (he belongs to Heaton Middle Pit) which first hit his head, and falling upon his legs had fractured the fibula of one, and cut the other down in a flap from a little below the knee to nearly the ancle, laying the shin bone bare for about 6 inches ... I put it up very carefully but if it unites by the first intention, I shall consider it almost a miracle. It is the most extensive flesh wound I ever saw. After I had dressed it my patient complained very much of the other – the fractured limb. I of course could only apply lotion to it and lay it in a proper position. No leeches are to be had.

A congregation of accidents

I have not done yet with accidents though of which a greater congregation have occurred this last week than I ever recollect since coming to Mr McI. There were two yesterday which I have not mentioned as they were slight. One man had his wrist sprained by the fall of a corf full of coals. The other was hurt on the shoulder from a blow. Both were able to come into town. A man also was killed at Elswick this morning but as he was dead when found the folks had the sense not to send for 'the Doctor'. A coal was laid upon his head which had most probably fractured his skull.

Today when I was just sitting down to dinner ... a horseman summoned me off to Walker to a person whose foot & leg were bruised by the fall of a coal. This accident however was not very severe. NB. I did not go till I had got aboard a good cargo of fish roast pig & bread pudding. A surgeon should never go to a

patient with an empty stomach else the chance that whilst his fingers are upon his patient's pulse or exercising their 'tactus' on a broken bone – his eyes are wandering into the cupboards or towards the bread loaf (mayhap a spice cake) and teapot which are generally in the way when a lamed man is brought home.

The great toe was dislocated

On Thursday night about 10 PM I was called to an accident at Heaton. The patient's right great toe was dislocated at the first joint. The swelling was exceedingly tense all over the foot; and, having no proper assistance I was after three or four vain attempts for want of mechanical force compelled to leave the luxation unreduced and apply leeches and fomentations. Next morning I got Mr Church – House surgeon to the Infirmary – to accompany me in my visit to the patient, and by our united strength together with that of another man we got the joint at last put right. Mr Liston says he would rather reduce a dislocated thigh than one of these above named cases; he thinks it is best to spend little time in vain attempts at reduction, but to cut down at once on the lateral ligaments and divide the opposing bands. In justice to myself I might say that both Mr Church & the patient agreed that it was impossible I should have reduced this bone (especially while unassisted) the night before.

Mr Liston was a famous surgeon, and one of Thomas's teachers at Edinburgh.

A fractured skull at Wallsend Pit

A young man at Wallsend was suffering from concussion after a mining accident. He was being treated but, about a week after the accident, his condition deteriorated and the doctors were called urgently.

On Saturday morning I was ordered 'to horse and away' to Wallsend. Mr King was to hold himself in readiness to mount the driving box of a hackney coach and in half an hour we found ourselves, i.e. Mr McIntyre, Mr Church, Mr King and myself, at the Wallsend Pit. Word had been sent from Hunters that the boy continued much worse and our intent was to propose an operation to the friends. On examining the skull (I had not disturbed the patient by doing so before being told. Mr McI said it was not fractured) there was a feeling like the edge of a fissure on the opposite side of the head to that on which the blow was received. The patient was insensible. He had been rather furious but as the compression on the brain became more powerful he subsided into the torpid state in which we then saw him. The father after an argument of near half an hour with Mr McI & Mr Church would on no account allow any operation to be attempted so we were obliged to leave the lad to the inevitable fate which the operation of the trephine it was then thought afforded a possibility of averting.

Yesterday morning the father came to the Surgery to say that the young man died about 4 AM and that if Mr McI wished he might now examine his head. I was down the Shields road at the time but King met me on my way home and we turned back. We were there in about an hour followed by Mr McIntyre.

A trephine, or trepan, is a very ancient instrument for cutting a hole in the skull to relieve blood pressure caused by an injury. Thomas gives a detailed description of the autopsy they carried out, concluding that the injury had been too severe for the proposed operation to have had any chance of success.

An awkward fall

… A patient came into the surgery last night in an awkward predicament. He had fallen from the scaffolding at the side of a hay stack and come into contact with some forks below – one had gone nearly through his wrist another had slightly penetrated his thigh while a ladder in falling struck him on the head and neck which were bruised in consequence. He had walked into town from Walker and was in the hay field this morning superintending the stacking. I ordered him fomentations & poultices by which he is relieved.

A bone in the throat

This is the only case mentioned in the Diary where a patient was sent to the Infirmary.

I was on Wednesday called in to a person at Wallsend who was reported to have swallowed a bone while supping some mutton broth last Sunday. I examined her throat with my fingers but could not go down as far as the point where she complained of pain. Mr M'Allum, surgeon, Wallsend, had been called in on Sunday and had maintained that no bone was in the passage but that it might perhaps have scratched the Pharynx in its way down. From symptoms I judged a portion of the bone was stuck fast but desired the woman might come to Newcastle to have the requisite instruments used for investigating the subject. Mr McIntyre however went down with me in the gig next day and after fruitless attempts to extract any bone or to get a probary passed in consequence of the great swelling of the parts and the contraction of the passage. Mr McI desired she might come up to the Infirmary. Mr Leighton examined her there on Friday morning but upon hearing she was our patient (he and Mr McI are not upon good terms) determined that no bone was there – that, forsooth, an abscess had formed in the pharynx causing the present symptoms. The patient had felt the bone on Monday with a quill and in her efforts had pushed it a good deal further down her throat. Mr McI thought he felt it at one time deep in the oesophagus but being surrounded and enclosed by swelling could not lay hold of it with his forceps.

Today, – the eighth day from her tasting food, the utmost extent of what she has taken through the week being about a cupful of liquids, – I took down the stomach pump and after Mr McI had passed a small flexible gum tube down the oesophagus I injected first about a pint of coffee and afterwards a similar quantity of sago. The patient had felt little hunger during her long fast but expressed herself 'comfortable' when the boiled sago had been given. She is taking a solution of Muriatic acid [*hydrochloric acid*] to attempt to dissolve the bone, upon the supposition that a piece is lodged still in her throat.

About a week later, Thomas reported that the bone had been dislodged and that 'the patient has been rapidly convalescent'. Mr Thomas Leighton, then aged 64, was a long-established doctor Newcastle and Head Surgeon at the Infirmary.

Newcastle Infirmary at Forth Bank, founded in 1751 was treating about 1500 patients a year in the 1820s. One house surgeon, and the nurses and domestic staff, were paid but the physicians and surgeons were local doctors who gave their services free.

The job – diseases and treatments

Mr Brown is very ill

At the time of the Diary, there was little understanding of the causes of illness and methods of diagnosis were primitive. 'Cures', used since the earliest days of medicine, often attempted to 'purify' the body, or bring it 'into balance' by purging, vomiting and bleeding. Mr Brown of Wallsend was given the full treatment. Nowadays, most of the purgatives mentioned are considered too violent for internal use, and worse, calomel (mercurous chloride) and antimony tartrate are known to be very toxic.

EXCELLENT MEDICINE FOR A BILIOUS COMPLAINT.

℞. Extract colocynth   -   - gr. viij
    Calomel   -   -   - gr. iv
           Mix. fiat pills ij.
      Capiat alternis nocte mitte ij.

  Take these two pills two times in the week, or for two weeks, and the following mixture at the same time. The day you take the pills omit the mixture for an adult.

From 'Every Man His Own Doctor'.

Thomas listed the medicine that had been taken before he saw the patient, and pretty violent stuff it was: purgative mixture containing 2 ounces of castor oil with 3 grains of antimony tartrate, an infusion of senna with magnesium sulphate (epsom salts), and ten compound Colocynth Pills, besides some purging medicine. Later the same day, he reported further on the case.

[Monday] ... a call came for me to go down to Brown, Wallsend. He was very ill from not having had his bowels open since Friday. He had his leg hurt some time ago, but was getting well of it, when he was attacked on Saturday with a pain in the side & bowels. Mr McIntyre bled him ... I took down the forcing syringe, and used it twice during the two hours I staid by him. I had not then

relieved his bowels of their load, tho' a slight evacuation had in great part removed the pain. Mr McIntyre has seen him and bled him again this afternoon and they are to send in at six o' clock to say how he is.

6 PM. They have come in from Brown. He has had no passage. Been in the warm bath; 7 minutes only. Could not bear the syringe to be used after I left. It seems he took a shillings worth of castor oil too yesterday. And some pills with Ol: Croton in each today. If not eased before morning Mr McIntyre has ordered a tobacco enema. And some Powders. Also croton oil pills as before. Also more purging mixture with added ammonium carbonate.

The powders contained ten grains of calomel and ten grains each of powdered scammon root and powdered gamboge root

At last, two days later, something began to happen.

Brown has had copious evacuations and is greatly relieved, but is still taking Croton oil and purging mixture.

Poorly children

Thomas often had to attend sick children, and was sometimes baffled by their condition. Early in his Diary, he described the symptoms of a disease he was meeting frequently and trying to treat.

The treatments were the usual purgatives and antacids. Some of the little patients did recover – probably in spite of rather than because of Thomas's medicines. But he did his best!

This Disease … I have chiefly met with in children teething, and from 2 to 16 months old. The symptoms are Diarrhoea (tho' sometimes in the first instance Constipation), evacuations of a green unnatural color, often mixed with blood; great listlessness; more or less cough & sickness; as the disease advances, the breathing becomes hurried; the head affected, apparently hydrocephalic, the eyes glazed & insensible; partial Hemiplegia; and the patient dies sometimes comatose at others apparently of suffocation. The pulse throughout is quick & feverish, and the mouth sore. The appetite disappears, but great thirst annoys the little sufferer. In two cases Hydrocephalus seemed the principal & idiopathic part of the affection, had it not been for obstinate diarrhoea which prevailed.

An epileptic boy

At the time, orthodox medicine recognised at least nine types of epilepsy, believed to have different causes, including head injury, pain, masturbation, and worms.

There is an interesting and well-marked case of epilepsy on the books just now arising from worms. The boy, about 7 years old, some time ago got rid of one large worm but lately has been attacked every night and frequently during the day with fits. He has partially lost the use of the left side. Mr McIntyre ordered him some Jalap & Calomel last week with a Rhubarb & Magnesia mixture which being taken without effect. I yesterday prescribed the following on the supposition that more worms remain which are causing the disease.

Thomas wrote into his Diary his prescription – for a violent purgative mixture, including calomel. A few days later, he returned to see his patient.

The epileptic patient mentioned has found great benefit from the use of those Croton Oil powders. The paroxysms when I saw him on Friday – when he had taken four powders – had returned less frequently and the dejecta were extremely unnatural and tar-like. Thinking that 6 grains of Calomel a day might be too powerful for a boy of his age I ordered the medicine to be repeated in a rather different formula. The other powders had not been very powerful.

Ainesly's boy (Epilepsy) is better in regard to his original disease but I find his tongue very foul this morning but of a different appearance to the fur at first exhibited and which last had almost disappeared. This today shewn is a thick softish white coating whilst the former one was brown & dry. I should judge the stomach now to be weakened by the severe medicines it has been necessary to use and have accordingly prescribed for him tonic medicine

Measles

Measles was then a serious, life-threatening, disease and a frequent cause of infant death.

The late bleak March weather and the prevalence of measles to a great extent with an ephemeral epidemic fever (principally amongst the females) has rendered our list of patients more than usually numerous. I am happy to say that one solitary case is the only instance of fatality in any of the above complaints – one child died in the measles. Those who had any tendency to weaklings have been sorely tried in the last three weeks and very many cases of lingering consumption terminated their career for ever.

An advertisement from the Newcastle Courant, 25th November, 1826.

A summary method of tooth drawing

Doctors at the time often did dental work. Tooth extraction was usually the only option for anyone with bad toothache. And of course it was done without anaesthetics. Thomas does not often mention this aspect of his work, probably because it was considered inferior to other types of surgery. However, he thought one innovation was worth mentioning.

I have this afternoon tried upon a poor odontalgic damsel the effect of Mr Fay's summary method of tooth drawing by nipping off their bodies with his awful looking forceps. Mr McIntyre got a set of these lately and used them unsuccessfully upon a lady's jaw nor have I so far better reason to think favorably of the plan.

Two days later there had been an improvement.

I am very glad to have to recant the assertion I made yesterday of Mr Fay's apparatus. The patient then mentioned today declares that as soon as she got home the tooth became quite easy and has not troubled her since. Should the plan be effectual it is undoubted a less painful operation than the extraction of the whole tooth.

Luckily, this treatment does not seem to have caught on!

A swollen knee

… I have seen a patient this morning with a chronic 'white swelling' of two month's standing in her left knee. Mr McI has had her under his care about a week, and has applied the Liniment Sapon to the limb. It is to be placed too on one of our ever useful splints! I should like very much to try the effect of a moxa or two upon the disease. The Soap Liniment however has made it no worse, but if Mr McI gets it bent upon the splint he will find it an awkward job, should anchylosis supervene, to get it back into its present straight position. I have lately heard an account from the patient himself (an old schoolfellow & intimate friend) of the inconveniences resulting from the limb being allowed to anchylose in a semibent posture.

A French remedy

Some two or three months since I applied to a patient a French remedy I had seen used by Dr Knox with considerable relief and was happy in obtaining a similar success. Having mentioned the circumstance to Mr Church, and recommending to him the perusal of a work on the subject with which I have been much interested (Wallace on Moxa) he requested me to operate on a patient in the infirmary who is in every way a fit subject for the experiment by way of making trial of the effects. The operation consists of burning a piece of pith or rolled lint upon the skin with a blowpipe and is very successfully employed by continental surgeons.

Prejudice is the only assignable cause of Moxa not being in general use among English practitioners, but it is scarcely known among our materia chirurgica.

The treatment called Moxa originated in traditional Chinese medicine where it is still used. Usually a small cylinder or cone of dried mugwort leaves is burned, rather than the pith or rolled lint used by Thomas.

I will try auscultation

At Byker Town I have a patient whose symptoms though by no means urgent rather puzzle me. I think there is some affection of the Heart or disease of the Ventricular Valves or Aorta. I will try auscultation if I have opportunity. Mr Church having been so polite as to return a stethoscope Mr McI had given him (he has now got several more) to me for my use.

The stethoscope (pictured below), at this time a wooden tube with bell and diaphragm, used to listen to sounds from the heart or chest (auscultation), later became probably the best known symbol of a doctor. In 1826 it was just coming into general use, a few years after it was invented by the French physician, Laennec.

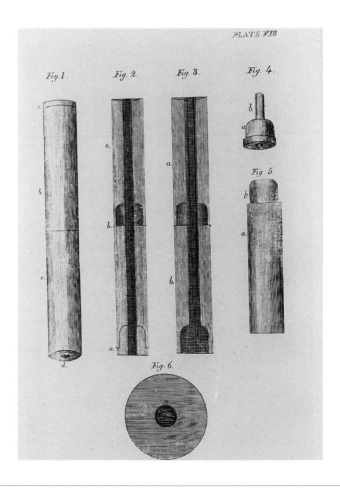

A badly fractured leg

In November 1827 Thomas had to attend to a miner at Heaton called Ramshaw, whose leg had been broken in a pit accident. His description of the progress of this case gives some idea of the pain and misery a broken leg could cause in those days, before the causes of wound infection were known.

After examining the injury so as to ascertain its exact extent ... I ... reduced the fracture, having cleansed the wound, and taken away, with the help of my scalpel, two tolerably large splinters from the tibia, laid the leg upon the splint, thus leaving all open for Mr McIntyres' inspection, and yet having only the bandages to be put on should the position &c be approved. When Mr McI came he ... said it was very well reduced ...

Two weeks later.

The bones had slipped from their apposition, the apposite surfaces being very small after the splinters had been extracted. I reduced the bones and having dressed the wound put on the bandages with additional cards & splints so as to prevent if possible the recurrence of any displacement.

The wound obviously became badly infected and, as Thomas mentioned from time to time, continued to give trouble. About 7 months after the accident the situation was still bad.

Ramshaw after one or two very severe & dangerous attacks of inflammation is still unable to get on his crutches. He sits up an hour or two daily ... This poor man is still in a bad state. Another large opening was made on Sunday the effect of which can not yet be ascertained. His constitutional health is better than for some years past but the limb continues obstinately intractable under every application. Patient sits up an hour or two daily and a chair is in preparation to enable him to get the fresh air out of doors.

The last mention was more than 11 months after the accident.

Ramshaw has had a severe attack lately of inflammation in his limb but it is today considerable abated. He gets out a little just to the door in an arm chair but is not able to use crutches.

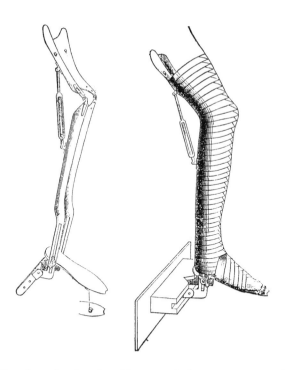

The type of splint for a broken leg illustrated above, was a modification of one invented by Mr McIntyre. It was reported in The Lancet in 1837 shortly after McIntyre's death: 'The apparatus ... was originally invented by M'Intyre, whose career of honourable usefulness has been lately suddenly arrested by death, and whose loss will be lamented by several members of the profession.'

Mrs Archbold has convulsions

… I was only last night wishing for 'something to do' when a man made his appearance all in a foam to fetch 'the doctor' down to a woman who was dying. Mr McI could not find in his heart (his love of the sex is so great) to go; and accordingly I set off with all convenient speed to Ouseburn. A woman near 'confinement' of her first child had distressed herself with the idea of her husband being in a consumption, in consequence of Mr McI's having ordered him a sea voyage in the morning. She had come up from Walker Gate, her residence, to her Mother's at Ouseburn. There she was seized with Puerperal Convulsions. She was in one of the paroxysms when I got down. I called for a bason & bandage immediately to bleed her. A Mr Wilson, Druggist &c &c of the village, who had been sent for in the interim (till someone from head quarters should arrive) had however saved me the trouble, and given her some antispasmodic medicine. As nothing further could be done while the fit lasted, I made the best of my way back to see Mr McI and sent him down; not wishing to have the responsibility of the case on my own shoulders. He went down. The person has continued in a succession of convulsive fits thro' the night; being so much worse about 12 oclock that they called us up, and got some change of medicine. She has had no return since 9 AM, and Dr Headlam who has just seen her (12 PM) has ordered her some aperient medicine and considered her out of danger. A slight degree of sensibility was perceptible when the messenger came away with the Drs prescription. Mr McI is gone off to a consultation at Penshah and has not therefore seen her since last night. I was called up to an accident at 5 this morning and precluded the necessity of Mr McI's called upon our patient till he returns from Painshaw by seeing her then. A more deplorable sight I think I have never witnessed than the distortion produced with this poor woman's convulsions.

Thomas's difficulties in spelling Penshaw were the least of his problems!

Doctor Headlam, a well-known local physician, from a contemporary drawing.

An original song

In going along the road, singing, soliloquising &c as usual, I caught myself up beside the Heaton High Pit in the middle of something like an original song and lest it should never get more into a finished state than the one in which it first struck me I will pop it down so far as a memorandum. Perhaps I may sometime improve upon the idea by introducing other scenery upon similar occasions exemplifying a round among my colliery patients. The expressions are so far (and I should like when my muse pays me another of her very rare visits to continue the same plan) the ordinary expressions used by the Pitmen on such occasions. There was a fragment of another verse but it will require alteration.

Air – 'Calder Fair'

Howay now here's the Doctor come for to see wor Nanny
Joe gang an hand the Doctor's horse there's a blithesome mannie.
Now Doctor how d'ye do sur, 'Here's a verra blawy day
Come by the fire an warm yorsel for need it weel ye may.'

'Well how's your Wife?' 'I thenk ye sur we think she's a vast better.
She was wanting sair to be out the day but aw thought ye wad not let her.
The Powders did a deal o' gude. The bottles dune also
And whether she'll need ony mair why yere the best to know sur.

She's got a nice bit happetite an's thrivin now awain sir
She'll awmost be for in t'town ayen ye come again sir.'
'You must just go on improving now you're doing very well.'
'When next'll ye be here sur, I'm sure I cannot tell.'

Shoals, bogs and pitfalls

Thomas described some of the trials of a young apprentice who had to dispense medicines in his master's 'shop' and get them to patients. He titled this extract 'More Miseries'.

Carrying out medicine to a distant part of the suburbs, and finding after you have rapped at the patient's door and put your hand into your pocket to deliver the mixture that was intended for the patient's stomach, now lines the inside of your surtout and the back of your trowsers.

Discovering on a similar occasion that you have left a small box of pills at the last house which you ought to have brought here and must go back for.

Puzzling to divine the reason why a mass which you ought to have ready for an impatient patient in two minutes and have been rubbing, and pounding at for a quarter of an hour – will not form into pills; when in the midst of the taunts on your slowness, and your own chemical speculation on the non-amalgamation of your substances, you perceive you have used the *blue-ointment* jar for what should have been the *blue-pill*.

Driving a cork too hard into a bottle, (which has cost you much pains in compounding) whereby it bursts to the grievous discomfiture of your pantaloons, and the loss of your time and temper and your master's property.

Taking a sup out of a bottle to wash a pill down your throat, which tastes nasty at the root of your gullet, and perceiving (if you have any breath left to think at all) that your mouth is full of Spirit of Hartshorn instead of Cinnamon Water.

On your return from a wet walk after a 'hard day' in the shop, finding a Draught for the farthest off patient you have just been at, and 'to be taken immediately' left lying on the counter.

The pleasant feeling of sleepiness consequent on you having swallowed a glass of Paregoric instead of Tincture of Ginger, by way of a morning cordial; and knowing of no one being near to get you an emetic, which you are too overpowered to get yourself, and are aware it is the only thing that you may avert the fatal effect of your draught.

The vain endeavours of anyone to form the 'Plummers Pills' according to the Pharmacopaeia of 1809 these ordered to be made with Balsam instead of Spirit which is the only proper solvent as many poor gentlemen know to their cost.

Contemplating the effects of a Dose of 12 grains of Calomel which you have half an hour ago sent out in 'two pills to be taken immediately' instead of in *eight* pills of which two were the dose.

After sending out two phials of one hartshorn oil, and one of manua & senna; the *exposée* that the labels have been unfortunately misplaced, and the child had so many spoonfuls of liniment crammed down its throat; instead of the opening mixture.

The nauseous feeling about the stomach on seeing 'oxalic acid' on a bottle out of which you have a few minutes before swallowed a dose of Epsom Salts; though the label had been stuck there by a wag in the interim.

Making salves occasionally; and Beating the Great Mortar at all times.

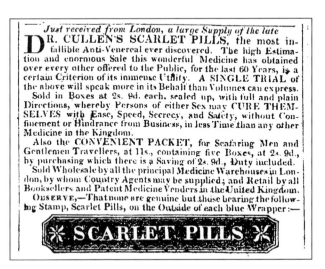

From Newcastle Courant, September 9 1826.

Getting Around

My new mare

Running the wide-spread practice depended on horse transport. Although Mr McIntyre kept two or three mounts for his staff, they didn't always come up to Thomas's expectations. However, he became very fond of the horse that he had at about the time he began his Diary, in spite of some problems with it.

My mare is getting a very bad habit of running away before I get mounted, which she did today and after a deal of difficulty (notwithstanding I was just laid across her, like a calf on a butcher's horse, length ways), got me off. The shock completely deprived me of breath for a few moments however I luckily came off in the end with a bruised finger, and a dirty great coat, which I got brushed at a patient's house close by. I have had leeches on my finger, and am writing this with it (the forefinger of my right hand) bandaged up.

The mare was still lively 2 months later.

My mare not having been out of the stables yesterday, was quite wild this morning, and chose to make a pig, which was walking quietly past, the pretext for breaking away from the woman who was holding it at a door and indulge itself with a half mile gallop on the road towards home again. Luckily a man caught it at Byker Gate where I got it after having walked all the way from Byker Hill for it. As it galloped so far for its own pleasure I determined it should have another gallop for mine accordingly I tamed it a little before we got home.

Get a gig down

Sometimes, there weren't enough horses to go around, and Thomas had to find some other way of getting to his patients.

An accident yesterday morning at Wallsend at 11 AM; Mr McI was at Benwell, and said he would be home soon … I waited till 1 for him. The other mare was getting shod so I had nothing to ride either, if I had wished to go sooner. Mr McI said nothing about going till near two when he told me to 'get a gig down' (giving me a half crown) to my not small chagrin; as there were then two horses in the stable. He said however that he should want one, and the other was not to go out at all yesterday, having had a hard day's work the day before .

I came down upon the hard road

Thomas had a gap of ten days in his Diary that he explained in his entry for Saturday, June 30 1827.

Something more than common must have happened to cause this long silence and something more than common *has* happened I must assure you gentle reader. On Sunday last I and my horse with all the paraphernalia of saddle, bridle &c came down upon the hard road with considerable impetus. Whether it was that the horse trod upon a sharp stone which pricked his conscience or that the sanctity of the day alone caused the deed, but certain it is that this said animal suddenly took it into his holy head to kneel in such a way as to cause great detriment both to his holy knees and to my elbow. I gave him a very righteous pull but only succeeded so far as to pull the pious animal over onto his side and on to my leg. The curve of the saddle formed an arch over my limb which saved it from harm, but I received as aforesaid 'a contusion of the arm with a slight abrasion of the cuticle' which is not yet quite healed. Luckily there has been no accident till yesterday morning and as my patients are all well or doing well they have found no want of me.

I walked down to Wallsend & Heaton on Tuesday. Mr McI desired me to ride so far in a Shields gig and return by the same conveyance; but the day was so pleasant I preferred walking down, and as I could not meet with a gig back I was obliged to trudge it both ways.

Thomas's recovery was helped by a present from his married sister, who lived in London.

Yesterday I received by the Hylton Joliffe (the newly started steamer from Newcastle to London) a parcel from my sister containing among other things a large plumb cake – a very excellent specimen of Islington confectionary; which fact is visibly demonstrated by its rapid dissolution.

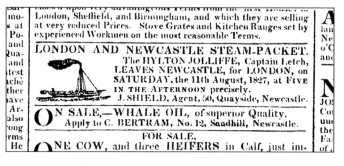

The Hylton Jolliffe advertised in the Newcastle Courant 11 August 1827.

Horse market day

Acquiring a new horse could be as chancy as buying a second-hand car is nowadays.

One of our great fairs began on Saturday and yesterday was the horse market day on the moor. I went to Heaton &c on my old friend the black horse but on coming home found a man waiting to take him away for good and altogether. Mr McIntyre was at the moor all day with his groom looking out for a new gig horse as I understand. They had made some sort of exchange between the black horse and a little brown mare which was accordingly installed in his place, but I hope not in his office of carrying me … I thought it was unlikely the animal before me would be able to trail the heavy gig which its master required in one of its station of life. These cogitations were dispelled however by the appearance of a tall chestnut colt towards evening. The little mare no doubt is for Mr Cochrane who has been on the lookout for a new one, and the chestnut 4-year old a genteel looking affair and which I shall forthwith christen 'Bayard' will have the honour of serving under me.

Sadly, Bayard was a disappointment.

This beast, – he is unworthy of the name I gave him and I therefore unchristened him – is good for nothing but carrying a dutchman, to which occupation he has most likely been accustomed. He splanders (if I may be allowed this expressive word) out his forelegs as if he wished to throw them away and can trot full four miles an hour without a stop!! Mr McI says 'he goes very well for a young horse' – 'Yes Sir' replied I 'but he takes an immense deal of driving'. My 'yes' however went a little against my conscience I only wish Mr McI to ride him one journey. I am satisfied the animal would never have the honour of carrying its owner again.

A new mare called Fanny

Thomas became very attached to a new horse he got in November 1827.

I have just now got into regular working trim a new mare and the chestnut horse I before spoke of has been sold. He was offered and shewed and displayed at two fairs but no dealer would (according to their expressions) 'look at him'. At last he is sold and a pretty little black nag Mr McI had bought nearly a month since but so far used entirely in the gig has now become my steed. By careful tuition and kind treatment I have brought this one already into a degree of docility I hope yet to improve upon. Though I have only ridden her 10 days the animal will follow me along the road without any hold of the reins and stand at the patients doors till I come out following me from one to another like a dog. As yet I dare not place much confidence in her fidelity but in a little while these qualities will be found extremely useful in a surgeons steed. The former practice too is useful on frosty days when a walk is pleasant to relieve the cold inactivity of the saddle. After puzzling my head in vain for a classic appellative for this favorite I at length fixed upon plain 'Fanny' by which she is conscious of being spoken to.

Sadly, poor Fanny had a bad fall the following Spring, and was given some medical treatment usually applied to human patients.

'Fanny' continues lame – her lameness being produced by a blister put on after her fall. She was used in the gig immediately on the application of this and the consequence was an inflammation of the whole limb and subsequent infirmity.

I have had a pit galloway on trial for a day or two; but on my unfavourable report being seconded by the groom's, it was returned as deficient in action. I shall be sorry to lose my old favorite and hope she may by time and gentle usage get sound though she never will be safe.

Thomas didn't mention Fanny again until nearly a year later, just before he left Newcastle.

As for our old friend Fanny, she has suffered a woeful change thanks to the Doctor's gig and hard driving. I rode her a short time since, and was very sorry indeed to find her paces so broken up, though she is in good condition and looks well.

The gig was overturned

One day in May 1827, Mr McIntyre and his sister Mary had a nasty accident.

Mr & Miss McIntyre were down at Tynemouth and about to return home when in taking off the horse's bridle (a wrong one had been put on) whilst both were in the gig, the horse set off at full speed without any bridle on. Mr McI having directed his sister to sit still leapt out and attempted to seize the horse's head but was thrown down and the wheel passed over his body. By this his arm was severely bruised also his side and his brow & nose deeply scratched. Miss McI fared worse. The horse carried her – now on the footpath & now on the road – about a mile making some turns very cleverly. At one sharper than the rest Miss M was projected out and most fortunately for in a hundred yards more the gig was overturned and the horse thrown quite on to his back with great violence breaking the gig & harness very much. The lady's side was severely bruised and her face but slightly. After being leeched & bled in consequence of an attack of inflammation in her chest she is able to sit up today. Mr McI does not shew himself much on account of his piebald face, which I have to dress night & morning; otherwise he is quite well again.

Winter rounds

The patients had to be visited, whatever the weather. A trip to Benwell meant going up the steep West Road, very difficult in late November 1826.

I was yesterday out at Benwell in one of the most bitter snow storms I ever encountered ... Mr McI said 'you will have the young man at Benwell to see sometime this morning you know', so, as the day did not look at all likely to improve, I set off directly, thinking the sooner I got my visit paid the better. I armed myself well against the cold, but the North wind upon exposed road, with thick, heavy snow was bitter to face. The storm was a good deal abated as I came back.

This morning was a beautifully clear frost. As the mare was not sharped, and the roads very slippery, I agreed with Mr McI that it would be safer walking to Benwell, and a delightful walk I had. The sun was powerful, shining in a cloudless sky, and the air 32° if not lower. I called at Green Field Place as I went up the Hill on my way out of town.

The roads were still difficult two days later.

My horse and I had a complete skaiting of it to Benwell again this morning. The snow having melted left only a hard stratum of smooth ice below, making the roads if anything worse than yesterday. I durst not ride down the bank to

Looking down Westgate road, the steep road up to Benwell, c.1820. Greenfield Place is behind the houses on the right.

the Benwell stables, but led my mare sliding down. It seems like a frost tonight, if so the horses must be sharped tomorrow or there will be no such thing as riding at all.

It was just as bad going to Byker.

After 'a real to do' Mr McI & I got down as far as Byker last night in the gig; the road was very slippery, and I was in full expectation of the mare coming down with gig and all her precious burthen. Mr McI left me at Catterick's buildings and said he would meet me at Byker Hill 'shortly'; I meantime seeing the patients about there. After waiting an hour at Byker Hill Mr McI came, but it was only to tell me I need not go farther. He was going down to Shields, and I was to meet him at Wallsend this morning at twelve oclock …

As I had the boy at Benwell to dress and to be down at Wallsend at 12, I was out early this morning, performing my West ride before breakfast. I rode down the Shields road with Tyler and was at the place of meeting an hour & half before Mr McI, though I was half an hour behind time, not expecting him to be very punctual. I was to see certain patients, he would see others and both were to be home as fast as possible. We subsequently met on the way home and rode into town together at full speed, splashing the dirt about in regular style. I came home in a pair of literal mudboots i.e. a case of mud over my topboots.

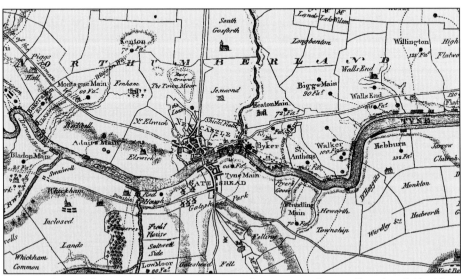

Newcastle and the surrounding area in 1804. The main road to Wallsend and Shields can be seen clearly.

Night visits were made reluctantly in bad weather, but a private patient had to be seen in January 1827.

A message was twice sent in from St Anthonys yesterday for Mrs Eliott, Mr Sewell's Housekeeper, to be seen – she was worse … As Mr McI was down that way I concluded that he would see this patient. He had said on going away in the morning he would be home at 3 PM … Upon the second of the above messages coming, about 7, I supposed he must be at St Anthonys which was the cause of his detention. I waited till 11 PM and was just going off to bed when I after a perplexing debate with myself formed the resolution of e'en going myself. On the road I met a messenger on horseback so that I was glad I had set off. The roads were a complete puddle – I had to go thro' several long fields – the night was hazy and the stars of the first magnitude & planets were barely visible – my eyes told me that I was on terra firma or something dark colored while my ears intimated that I was crossing some interminable river by the plodging of my horse's feet. As there was a man with me and I was going to the respectable housekeeper of a person of quality, I was obliged to 'get on' (as someone I know would say) so that on the whole I had a bumping sort of ride there. I bled my patient &c &c & left her easier. My ride back however was somewhat different. The sky was clearer – the air mild if not almost warm and I began very unconcernedly to sing most lustily, frightening all the crows, magpies &c for half a mile round … I got home just as the Charlies were bawling drawling or calling (each in his way) 'past two'. Mr McI had got home. I went to bed and slept soundly till – I woke.

The Newcastle watchmen – known locally as Charlies – were on duty between 10pm and 6am, going on rounds and calling out the time every half-hour.

Newcastle life

Saturday on the Shields Road

I was highly amused this morning on going out into the country about 10 oclock, (the first Saturday morning I have been out at that time) to observe the crowds of pitmen, their wives, & bairns coming 'to the toon', all in their 'Sunday cleais'. Here was a Jerry Sneak looking man with 'the bit bairn' in his arms, while his wife of more tummified dimensions luggs a large empty basket, destined to contain the ' few necessaries' for the ensuing week. There a group of lads with their hands in their breeches pockets going merely 'for pleesurin' or to buy a new hat or 'pair o' shoon' or get a new 'pick-shaft' &c. And others to 'have a pint with some friends'; which probably ended in Gallons. Two or three times I met large long carts with two horses tandem, completely laden with women & their baskets. On the Shields road there was a stream like that toward a race course on the cup day, or to Duddingston loch when frozen. My accostations from the parties were numerous; and the hat and hand were constantly meeting before me as I rode down.

'Jerry Sneak', a hen-pecked husband, is a character in a play entitled 'Mayor of Garrat or The Humours of the Army'. Duddingston Loch is in Edinburgh. Thomas went skating there, together with most of the population of the city, when he was in Edinburgh in January 1826.

'Here's a fine day, doctor!' … 'Hoo are ye, doctor?' 'Ye're in a hurry today doctor, is ought matter?' 'I say doctor, I wish ye'd give a caaal and leuk at the wife, she no'but badly the day, puir body. She does na reest weel at neights, but maybies ye'll see her as ye gang by' (Very well I'll see how she is but how's the lad now) 'Oh! thank ye sir, he gotten nicely soon, his appetite's coming round and he thinking o' trying wark o Monday, if ye hae nae objection like.' 'Holloa, doctor, ye need no caall at wor house, the wife's no in and aw's goan to try if aw can git as far as to toon, ye see, with this leg o' mine; it feels quite strong now, ye said ye'd order me a bottle to rub it with, if aw caall, I suppose t'lads i'nt shop can gie me't' (Oh yes, mind you don't get drunk now or else you'll be breaking the other leg and you'll have that job to pay for yourself you know) (How's your wife) 'She just her ordinary, thank ye sir, whiles better & whiles worse'.

Mayor choosing Monday

Being the first Monday after Michaelmas, it is the day on which 'wor new Mayor' is chosen, or as it is called 'Mayor choosing Monday'; when little bairns, (and many up-grown bairns), get dressed up as 'the Mayor', and go about begging halfpence. I have been gammoned out of twopence (luckily all the change I had) by two mayorified pitmen. For the benefit of the antiquarians of the next century, and others who may in after ages peruse this erudite composition, I may as well mention that on this day Archibald Reed Esq was elected to the right worshipful dignity of Mayor of Newcastle.

Barge Day 1827

Ascension day and 'par consequence' the day on which the Mayor of Newcastle sails round the boundaries of the port in his state barge and followed by a concourse of boats. The day is hereabouts known as the 'barge day'. This mayor being a great general favorite his barge day was expected to be more splendid than usual and I have just come up from viewing the procession. There are boats, and barges, wherries, gigs, luggers, steam vessels, keels, and every description of nautical pleasure boat, with flags of all colors sizes & shapes, the rowers chiefly in their peculiar uniforms. The mayor's &

Barge Day, from a painting by Thomas Carmichael.

the custom house barges of course formed the most conspicuous objects but the gaudy painted gigs and steam boats greatly aided to enliven a very busy and interesting spectacle. Three or four bands of music were in different parts of the river. The officers of the troops at present in the barracks had their galley with six oars and cut rather a prominent figure in their straw hats, striped shirts with black handkerchiefs, blue jackets & white trowsers. Among the prettiest of the gigs were the 'Venus', 'Harmony', 'Britannia', 'Caledonia' & 'Tyger'.

Gateshead Choral Society at All Saints

On Sunday afternoon I attended service at All Saints to hear the sacred music then and there to be performed by the 'Gateshead Choral Society'. About fifty formed the band. The opening chorus was very well sung and hence I anticipated a treat throughout. The church was as closely packed with people as the wood-work (the only space left not occupied by human beings) would permit;

All Saints Church in 1820.

and the congregation could not be far under 4000 people. The effect of the hundredth psalm in which most of these joined was sublime in the extreme, and I was in one of the best situations in the church for enjoying it. I anticipated a climax of rapture with the Hallelujah chorus of the Messiah which was to conclude the whole but never was any one more grievously disappointed. The counter tenors shouting, for roaring is too mild a term – bellowing is perhaps more expressive; and the altos and trebles squalling with the basses howling (those these last did acquit themselves the best if any) were altogether much too powerful for my ears and almost enough to destroy the effects of the previous music. Dr Gibbs of Durham preached a sermon for the benefit of the Church Missionary Societies and a plentiful harvest would be secured by the collectors I should think, though I have not yet heard the amount.

Death of the Duke of York

Frederick Augustus, second son of George III, the 'Grand Old' Duke of York of the Nursery Rhyme, died in January 1827. Thomas seems unimpressed by the pomp of the occasion.

On this day were committed to the Tomb the remains of his late Royal Highness the Duke of York and Albany Heir Apparent to the Throne of this Empire, Commander in Chief &c &c as the reader may learn by consulting the records of the day all margined with black upon the occasion.

There were notices in abundance of the forms to be observed on this day but very little regret seems to be shewn. The bells did toll certainly for about 10 minutes in the morning at the firing of one of the guns from the Castle, and the same was repeated this afternoon 'midst a salute from the cannon to the great amusement of a parcel of dirty lads gathered round to catch the burning tow as it fell, and the great annoyance of the good and peaceable towns folk who dwelt in the immediate vicinity of the ancient tower which gives name to 'wor gude toon'.

I have worn a pair of black trowsers all this week to be like other folk of similar gentility. I always wear a black coat and having as aforementioned got a new one not long ago in a very decent black. A piece of crape would have been useful in covering a grease spot on my hat but as the gazette does not mention hat bands as necessary for general mourning and I had not the honor of being particularly known to his royal highness I must go with my hat as it is.

The Tyne Huzzar Yeomen are up on duty

'The Tyne Huzzar Yeomen', officially called The Northumberland and Newcastle Volunteer Corps of Cavalry, was a direct ancestor of the famous regiment, The Northumberland (Hussars) Yeomanry, which fought in the Boer War and two world wars. The tradition of annual training for eight days on the Town Moor continued until the 1870s.

On June 18, 1827, the local militia were doing their training.

The cannons woke me this morning in announcing the anniversary of the battle of Waterloo which I suppose will in many places be fought over again today at the dinner table. The Tyne Huzzar Yeomen are to be up on duty for eight days commencing this morning. My friend Henzell is a cornet in that regiment.

Peacetime training was not without its hazards.

The Cavalry are very busy parading about this week amongst them of course *Cornet* McIntyre. Yesterday morning a man one of the troop was thrown from his horse while on duty on the moor and his horse falling upon him his ilium was fractured at the spine and his hip severely bruised. Surgeon Moore and Assistant Surgeon McIntyre have attended him and after prompt leeching he is today doing well.

Thomas seems to be mocking his boss's lowly rank of Cornet – Cornet McIntyre was promoted to Lieutenant in March 1829.

The poor woman was hung this morning

Jane Jameson, was found guilty of murder in March 1829, and executed by hanging in public. The dissection of her body by the medical profession was legally allowed. Members of the medical profession were admitted free, and the general public on payment of a fee.

A wretch has taken her trial today for the murder of her Mother; and it is reported that the monster killed her Father and two illegitimate children before this. She belonged to the Keelmans Hospital in this town where she perpetrated the crime for which she has this afternoon been condemned. I could not obtain access to the crowded court but I am told by one who was there that the unfortunate creature is condemned to execution on Saturday morning and to be given to Surgeon's Hall for dissection. If the latter part of the sentence be correctly reported I shall most likely partake of the benefits accruing therefrom.

The Newcastle Courant reported: 'The crowd that attended the execution was immense. We have heard the number of persons present estimated at 20,000, more than half of whom were women. The dreadful ceremony does not seem to have made on all who witnessed it the impression it should have made, for there were some pockets picked at the time.'

The poor woman was hung this morning at the old place of execution near the barracks. The procession passed along this street and within sight of my window but I had not the curiosity to join the assembled thousands who crowded to the last scene of her existence. The body will I suppose be exposed to public gaze for a few days when she will be anatomised by Mr Fife.

Jane Jameson as she appeared at the Bar on March 5th, 1829, on trial for the murder of her mother.

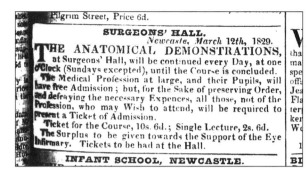

An advertisement for the anatomical demonstrations from The Newcastle Courant.

Mr John Fife on Monday noon gave a very good demonstration on the brain of the criminal who suffered on Saturday … Mr Fife as I have said acquitted himself well in his place as lecturer, and had a good opportunity, from the freshness of the brain before him, to exhibit its parts and structure in a clear manner, more so than usually falls to the lot of an anatomical teacher. Mr Geo: Fife holds the office of assistant to his brother. The audience altogether might be about 50 of whom almost one third were non professionals.

The fresh brain turned out to be the high point of the lectures. Thomas went to most of the series, but was somewhat disappointed. Perhaps he was comparing these lectures to those of Dr Robert Knox that he attended while he was a student in Edinburgh. Knox had a high reputation as a brilliant lecturer and teacher of anatomy

Surgeons' Hall, Newcastle, formerly the Barber Surgeons' Hall.

I was at church last Sunday

Thomas did not go to church regularly, often working on Sundays, and he does not name the church he attended most often, but it was probably St Andrew's, in Gallowgate. He seems to have been open-minded about religion, and attended services in churches of various denominations. Mr Turner's chapel was the Unitarian Church in Hanover Square.

I went to Mr Turner's chapel this morning. I was at Church too last Sunday, Mr McI being from home. I was in Mr Gibson's pew and heard a sermon from the vicar as usual. It was on behalf of the manufactures. I was feeling in my left hand pocket for a sixpence when the vicar told us that the churchwardens would come by houserow on the Tuesday following, which was perhaps as well for the fate of my sixpence. The worthy clergyman I thought rather unfairly made the amount of our subscription the test of our attention to and accordance with his sermon though he had just before said we were not to give through any motive but pure charity! I was out when they called on Tuesday.

Poachers on trial

The Assize Calendar for Newcastle 6 March 1827 lists Thomas Armstrong, aged 25, and Jonathan Campbell, aged 23, charged with unlawfully shooting at Francis Charlton. The case was assigned to the court at Gosforth.

The assizes have been held this last week. I managed to get to the courts once or twice. I heard a good part, – that is the beginning & end, of a trial in which both prisoners were of Benwell Colliery and in consequence had been patients of ours.

A thorough-bred rascal, Campbell had led off a young man into a poaching exploit, on Mr Brandling's estate. They were surprized by the game keepers, & Campbell was seized.

Armstrong, his companion, to release Campbell, fired at the legs of the keepers and both got off. Mr Moore & J Gibson attended the keeper who was severely wounded. Both the poachers were taken after a reward of £50 had been offered, by Campbells informing of his companion, who had fired to release him!! Campbell instead therefore of being hung or worse, which he richly deserved, was admitted King's Evidence and pardoned, getting also £50 for his villainy. The keepers could swear to Campbell, but not to Armstrong. His employers one and all came forward to give Armstrong an excellent general character, being fond of a gun was his only draw back. Campbell's evidence only being credited so far as corroborated by other witnesses, the Jury, after retiring for a long time, returned a verdict of 'Guilty of firing the gun'. His lordship however hesitating to receive that, the jury retired again, and after some further consideration returned a verdict of 'Not Guilty', on the plea of want of evidence I suppose.

At the races

Horse races were run on the Town Moor from 1721, and in Thomas's time there was a race meeting there during the week nearest to midsummer's day ('race week', now the time of Newcastle Hoppings fair). Thomas went to the races in 1827.

Tuesday 3rd July
Our Newcastle races began yesterday which will of course cause a little gaiety in the town this week. Mr McI, according to custom, offered me the use of the

horse I usually ride, which I, according to custom, accepted; as he has only been one day out of the stable since he and I happened our accident he was proportionally in high trim, and cut by no means a sorry figure among his numerously assembled brethren.

There were two very prettily contested races yesterday ... the Produce stakes was 'won easy'. Six horses started for 'The Tyro Stakes' which a son of the renowned Dr Syntax won. He was not the favorite but a grey filly took such a wide turn, or as it is technically termed 'bolted' by which she lost more ground than it was possible to make up again. The last race 'the Gosforth Stakes' was a neck and neck matter from the distancing post – only two horses ran.

Mr McI is gone to Tynemouth on my steed and will most likely not return till near race time. Mr King (William) would perhaps have the option of riding today but not having yet been on the saddle he prefers the safer way – going on foot. As the horse will not be so fresh I shall walk too.

Wednesday 4th July

The horse was not at home for either Mr K or me yesterday. Mr McI not returning till evening. We walked therefore and King having the offer of the horse today has ventured to mount and luckily came home with no injury more than a fright or two. I rode the steed about 10 or 12 miles this morning and took a little of the shine off him in compassion for Mr K. Mr Powlett's Gazebo (a horse I bet upon by chance for the Plate) won the King's £100 yesterday which is a four mile job and with very heavy weights. When the horses for the Stakes appeared to my great surprize my favorite Gazebo was again among the candidates and after a severe contest won both heats of this race!!

Today I laid out my profits of yesterday in bets and chose first the field against two horses neither of which ran and of course won. I also wagered a bottle of porter with Brockett upon the horse which won the Silver cup! All the heats today have been sharply contended for and hence the sport has been very good.

Friday 6th July

On Thursday I went on horseback to the Races and enjoyed the sport highly. The crowds of people were immense and the racing tolerably good. As usual the horse on which I bet won the Gold Cup! With all my winnings however I am not a farthing the richer. My wagers were in bottles of Porter, Pop &c and the only one I staked in money was left unsettled as to the amount and by that means my opponents Tyler & J. Gibson slipped off. Indeed I shall never have the face to ask a person for a bet in money; and hence had better not speculate any more in spece. In anything else too I have to treat as much as I have been treated with hence I get little profit in that way either.

A pleasant run with the hounds as far as Denton Burn

On his rounds one day in March 1829 Thomas had a pleasant surprise when he met the local hunt.

Yesterday I was lucky enough for the first time this season to meet with the hounds during my ride. They were passing near the Benwell stables and though I had to breast the hill to get into their track I soon overtook the rest of the sportsmen, and had a pleasant run as far as Denton Burn near Scotswood, where they lost scent and I left them. The pack (harriers) belonged to Mr Burdon, Sanderson, and were attended by Mr Clarke, Fenham, Mr Hazle, Denton, and about ½ a dozen other gentlemen. My young charger agreeably surprized me by his willing exertions. He was certainly fresh and in good trim, but from his shyness on the road I hardly expected him to face a hedge or a ditch, and began to funck for the respectability of my appearance when we should come at any obstacle of that sort; but Nebuchadnezzar had only to be turned to the fence, and he was over it in a trice nor did he refuse a single leap during our short run. Had he been prepared (by having no water &c) for a good wind and a brisk chace I should certainly have indulged my horse and myself by keeping the field till the last. As his wind was rather short from his morning's water I reluctantly, and to the no small disappointment of Nebby, evinced by many a prancing wish to turn back, – brought myself away, home, having seen my patients before I met with the dogs.

The Duke of Wellington visits Newcastle

Wellington, the great hero of Waterloo, made an official visit to Newcastle in 1827, twelve years after the battle. He became Prime Minister the following year.

The general topic of conversation just now is the Duke of Wellington's visit to Newcastle. He is to come in about 3 oclock this afternoon and to review the cavalry on the moor; after which there will be a great dinner at the Mansion House and ball at the Assembly rooms. The newspapers are so full of all the regulations &c that it is quite throwing away time for me to say much about the business here.

After the visit Thomas commented:

The great day has passed over and nothing particularly grand took place. An immense concourse of people was assembled but the afternoon was very unfavourable. I was in a window looking out to the Sandhill and with my companions at that window received a most polite bow from the Duke as he passed and on our kissing our hands to his Grace.

The Duke of Wellington.

At home, and going out

A dirty smoky hole

In 1828, Thomas described his room in Mr McIntyre's old house in Newgate Street, where he had been living since he came to Newcastle in 1824.

... a dirty smoky hole with a black ceiling – (from the gas); walls which could not upon a moderate computation have been papered or cleaned within the last century; a window seldom disturbed by brush or duster, and through which, if you could see any thing, it was only to count the stones in the opposite blank wall about three yards off, – for a glimpse of even sky much less sun you could hardly get; a fire-place which my antiquarian research opines me had once been black, but had been improved in course of time to all colors but white; a thing which I believe once had been a fender; but without irons or other appurtenance except what an old coal-rake shank stood instead of; a few old bookshelves which the dust and the flies had painted with an imitation of anything but wood; and finally the room hung around with a few pictures varnished with grease and glazed with soot and dirt ... The well inked uncarpeted

floor bears witness to [the writer's] industry, when illuminated often all day by the light of the gas – (often not illuminated at all,) he has sat for hours upon the hard solid wood chairs, poring over and extracting the sweets from some gem of science; or penning some lighter articles in his Diary.

Mr McIntyre's house, at 91 Newgate Street in 1879, by which time it had become the premises of Robson, licensed retailer.

The arduous task of moving

In August 1828, Mr McIntyre moved his establishment from Newgate Street to much better premises in the elegant and newly built Eldon Square.

Last Monday morning at 2 AM we commenced the arduous task of removing all the goods and chattels from our late abode. I was sent forward to take charge of the things as they arrived in the new house, and by seven oclock (a little before which Miss McIntyre came over) we sat down to a comfortable breakfast in a well furnished dining room. Almost all the furniture came over that day and on Tuesday I was busy superintending the putting up of shop fixtures &c. Wednesday was employed in sending over the contents of the cellar which was left to my care. On Thursday we all found time to spend a few hours on the moor to see the gold cup run for; but it was not till Saturday night that I could sit down in any sort of comfort in the new house. By that time I was completely worn out and have hardly recovered from the over fatigue of last week, and a complete drenching yesterday, which dose was repeated today.

Eldon Square c.1841.

Mr McIntyre moved his medical business to No. 1 Eldon Square (at the far right corner) in 1826. The house, then new and very fashionable, continued to be a doctor's residence for the rest of the 19th century, and is still recognisable today.

A new oil cloth has this afternoon been laid down on 'my room' floor; which now gives us a very respectable appearance, i.e., one befitting the dedication of the place, and the gentleman who inhabits it … I have a comfortable rush bottomed arm chair to sit down in (one or two to spare for a friend also) and the light of heaven and sunshine to enliven me; though I still cannot boast much of improvement in regard to prospect, a joiners work yard and saw pit being my vista, wood, & water. A pair of globes, pray take notice, ornament my sanctum, and all bears an air of comfortable usefulness. I must not omit to add that a good genteel set of fire irons and fender with a respectable grate and black marble chimney piece form part of our arrangements; and that good inside folding window boards have assumed the place of a queer dingy, black-brown, quondam green gauze blind with sundry rents and peep holes, which was all the protection our last settlement afforded. The new surgery, though, like the room above it small, is at last conveniently arranged; and when it gets its finishing coat of paint and I get my room papered, this part of the great house will have a genteel appearance not unworthy of the rest of the building.

Shopping

Shopping seems to have been as tedious for Thomas in the 1820s as it can be now.

I have … been nowhere today, except to get myself a chain-fastener for a cloak; and a curious hunt I have had after it. First at a drapers, who sent me to his neighbour; he had none; so I called at a clothiers, & furriers, who directed me to a Hardwaremans, who recommended me to a silversmiths, who happened to have what I wanted.

A new cloak

Amongst 'other things new' (a general question with some folks and almost the only one thing they utter – 'have you anything new?') I have got a new upper garment in the form of a Cloak; – 'Toga' my Mother calls it. I was afraid of some new and peculiar fashions being introduced in it, as it was made under my Mother's superintendence. Tho' I do not in the least doubt, but rather can bear witness to Mrs Wright's taste in female attire; yet a gentleman's winter costume in town can be so badly judged by a person in the country, that I must say I was rather afraid of it. I confess however I was 'agreeably disappointed' (for that is actually an English phraze) on receiving this said cloak which is bona fide a genteel thing. – I must write home tomorrow to make all right, and patch up the business the best way I can. I have got one sharp retort from my Mother already.

New shag trousers

'Shag' was a long-napped rough cloth. Capillaire is an orange flavoured syrup.

I must write home tonight about my intended new pair of 'inexpressibles', for Scarlett has none of the shag cord my Mother wants me to wear. One of my Mother's reasons is 'Does not Sir M W Ridley wear them?' That kind of argument always reminds me of an anecdote I heard some time ago. A Mrs W— wished her son to swallow (by way of making his breakfast slip down more readily, and partly because 'it was good for the inside', I suppose) every morning a wineglassful of sweet or salad oil!! Among other persuasions used to the unwilling patient was this, that Lady D–s & Mrs C–r gave their daughters the same. Some time afterward I happened to hear that the Miss C's used to take in a morning a wineglassful not of sweet oil, – but – Capillaire!! which Mrs W's informant had mistaken for oil. So much for a wrong precedent; and I fear it may turn out after all that it is Sir MWR's servants who wear this shag, as it is rather groomish stuff.

A week later – the trousers turned out better than expected.

Got home my new shag breeches – very comfortable winter wear – never mind stylishness they are genteel & warm.

Christmas

Thomas did not get a Christmas holiday, but there were some seasonal celebrations.

December 22 … Received a regular Christmas basket this morning from home. A Yule log, Yule candle, Yule cheese Yule cake, Yule cordial and many other yule-ish appendages … I am invited to dine at Mr Gibson's (Senr) on Christmas day.

December 23 … After making up a packet for Croft I have been down at Parson's &c as the shops will not be open on Monday [Christmas day]. Mr Crawford has been down to ask me to dine there on Monday – being engaged as above I accepted his invitation to sup in Greenfield Place on frumenty tomorrow evening. I have not seen a patient out of the Surgery today. As the Pits are now laid off till after Xmas we shall have little chance of accidents for a few days. A very slack week this last.

December 27 … What with visiting, accounts &c I have been closely employed since Saturday. I got the accounts made up so far as posted in Ledger last night, but they are all to add up and enter in a list yet so that I shall have little writing

Greenfield Place, behind Westgate Road, in 1960. In the 1820s these houses were part of a fashionable new development.

leisure this 10 days yet to come. I supped in Greenfield Place on Xmas eve and dined at Mr Gibsons on the following day. Both very pleasant meetings. We had a good round game (Loo) on Monday evening at which I just won back my stake. Mr Tyler, a Mr McCuller & myself were the only visitors. Wm

Gibson was home from Sedgefield. Miss G is away and has been some time. I was in hopes we should have had a dance but it was not named – there would have been a scarcity of ladies indeed. Misses Bell & Dorothy only to 5 gentlemen.

An invitation

As I came up street, Miss T, Miss G, Miss IG, Mr JG &c were standing in the window and presently after Jack came up to ask me to go down to tea at his lodgings – he expected some 'belles femmes' there. I popped out of my breeches into a pair of trowsers. Donned a clean collar & cravat and marched down to Mr John Gibsons lodgings. Mr Benj: Gibson presently entered followed by Miss Taylerson, Miss & Miss Isabel Gibson. We had tea & played a very pleasant game at cards afterwards. I and Fanny (G) lost a rubber & a game.

The people at the window were Thomas's colleague and friend John Gibson (Jack), John's sisters, Fanny and Isobel, and his girlfriend Miss Taylerson. Benjamin was John's brother.

I got set between two nice lassies

On Wednesday evening I went to a card party at Mr Brocketts and played a very pleasant game at Pope. About 26 ladies & gentlemen were there – who I know not. But I do know I got set between two nice lassies at the card table, enjoyed myself in laughing with them till my sides ached; and was obliged very reluctantly to tear myself away from pope and the pretty Miss Rutherfords about eleven oclock.

Pope, or Pope Joan, is a round card game. Charles Dickens described a lively game of Pope in Chapter Six of Pickwick Papers.

You can't go tonight

I have been drinking tea with J Gibson tonight and he has been trying hard to persuade me to go with him to the So: Shields ball on Tuesday. I feel half inclined never having stirred a foot in the way of a dance this winter. I want to try my hand at a quadrille too. If I go we are to drive down in a gig of Wm Greys (JG's cousin) and get home about 4 or 5 in the morning. I can say to Mr McI that I am wishing to go to a party. The tickets are only 4/- which I think I may afford upon a pinch. I must consider the matter well before morning.

On Wednesday, the day after the ball …

I had arranged everything for going down to this ball last night and only wanted Mr McI's assent to complete my expedition. I therefore said to him after dinner that 'I was wishing to go out tonight if nothing was wanted.' 'Umph you are not going far are you?' 'I have had a seat down to the South Shields ball offered, sir, which is held tonight.' 'Umph – why, I am going out myself tonight so that you can't go tonight.' 'Very well, sir', and accordingly I withdrew. JG was vexed at first and said I had prevented him going as he would not go by himself. He had however refused Mr Fryer Junr a seat in the gig in consequence of my agreeing to go and I suppose he did go with a gentleman, but as I have not seen JG since, I can't tell who this gentleman was. Mr McI was down at Wallsend in the evening.

A word to the wise

Thomas had an eye for pretty girls. Of course, he always kept within the strict conventions of the day, at least as far as his Diary reveals. But his mother must have been worried.

My Mother writing to me last week, gives me what she calls a 'word to the wise' about singeing my wings like a moth fluttering around a candle; alluding of course to some wings which Cupid may have lent or given me. This candle symbol however does not half suit me. Shade of Hellen!! A candle! to compare a ladies eyes, – sparkling like the finest jet, – dazzling like brilliants, or languishing in heavenly blue – to compare these, gentle reader – only think, – to what? to a candle! Yea even to a four mold, – the princess of candles!! And me courteous reader, to compare – to liken me to a moth – a sluggish good-for-nothing moth! The only explanation I can give is that my dear Mother must mean that rare and valuable insect in collections, the Death's Head moth which has a skull painted on its back, – hence is professional! I am, I flatter myself, no inattentive observer of human physiognomy especially of the most agreeable & interesting kind; but, so far, I have not found a star (and I have seen a great many of great splendour) powerful enough to set me in a blaze; or even 'to singe me'. I hold myself proof to everything but a very comet!! and that with a preterparticularly considerably long train. Something that will be worth stand my fire and 'singeing ones wings' for.

A pleasant evening

Spent last evening very pleasantly with a party at Mr Piles being invited two days ago 'to tea & cards'. The junta consisted of Messrs Lang, Henzell, Elwood & Pow of the old quorum and two new friends of Mr Flood a Norwegian merchant who has been sometime in Newcastle and is to leave it tomorrow – also a Mr Tebey. Henzell did not join us till late and as we could not till then make up two whist tables we drew cuts for who were to compose the complete game and the other three who were to form a three handed party. It fell to my lot to be of the latter class and I took as a trial the playing of the dumb hand for a partner. My opponents were Mr Flood and Mr Pow. If I won I got double stakes but this advantage was more than counterbalanced (considering I had never played two hands before) by my liability also to pay 'shots' for myself & partner should I lose the game. Stakes were as usual at our meetings sixpence per game. I won the first and second but lost a third when Henzell became my partner and he and I were victors again before supper was announced. I therefore was in the end plus 1/6. With toasting singing & speechifying the evening as I have said passed very pleasantly. I was the only one whose song (such as it was) was encored.

A brooch was stolen

On Friday week I was off early with Mr McIntyre to Backworth &c, whence we did not return till afternoon, and not requiring my breastpin I in my hurry left it sticking in the corner of my dressing glass, a place where indeed it often was kept for convenience. On going to my room at night I observed it to be wanting and made enquiry amongst the servants next morning. One girl had left the day before and she was said to have been last in my room so to her I sent word that if she did not return my brooch, a constable and search warrant would be applied to. She came into town yesterday to answer the charge and firmly asserts that the trinket was on my dressing table when she left the room that morning. Her, I confidently suspect of the theft; as certainly as I charge the cook who left last term with the taking of my other breast pin and silk handkerchief. I cannot, however, devise any plan of regaining the lost goods as they will be securely enough disposed of by this time.

This brooch is more valuable both in intrinsic worth and if possible on account of the donor (my dear Mother) than the last one I had stolen – an agate set in gold.

If any excuse for my not putting the brooch into a more safe place be wanted or allowed, I may state that I have in this large, new, inconvenient house, neither closet, drawers, or wardrobe of any kind to keep an article in. My trunks are occupied by my linen and other vestments, so that two open wash stand drawers are all I have upstairs to put anything of that kind into, and my writing box downstairs (four stories from my dressing glass) is an inconvenient receptacle for such ornaments.

I have not quite given up all hope – it is barely possible the brooch may have been mislaid or found in some way or other but such chance I fear is so slight as almost to amount to despair.

A paper at the Lit and Phil

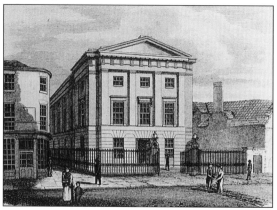

Thomas was a keen member of Newcastle's Literary and Philosophical Society, making good use of its library and attending many of the educational lectures it had on offer. In October 1827, he offered to present a paper himself.

On the second of this month, – being the month's meeting of the Lit: & Phil: Society I sent a paper to Mr Turner, stating that 'should nothing more important press upon the attention of the Society at their next monthly meeting' I intended doing myself the honor of laying before the members a model of a machine invented by my Father for drawing coals up the pit &c. My offer was very flatteringly accepted Mr Turner saying that the Society would feel obliged by any information regarding that subject and hoped I would bring the machine before them when convenient.

It was a big occasion for Thomas, then only 19, to speak before the intelligentsia of Newcastle and he was a bit apprehensive before his talk. But it went pretty well.

Last Tuesday evening passed off very much to my gratification at the Society's meeting. About 35 members were present forming the most numerous monthly meeting I have attended. Mr Boyd the Banker was president for the night and I was called to his and Mr Turner's right hand, taking possession indeed of the secretaries desk, to read my paper. I have had the pleasure of hearing nothing

The Lit. & Phil. c.1830.

but compliments from all who were present and I must say I was very well satisfied with myself on the occasion.

With the exception of the foregoing, no further notice has been taken of the machine. It has stood on the Society's table ever since the meeting and has been examined by many persons but I have not been applied to by any.

The machine is described in the minutes of the meeting as an 'ingenious invention … for raising water, coals &c without changing the direction of the power employed, or in any way endangering the safety of the workmen'. Unfortunately, in spite of the publicity, no one was rushing to buy.

A well-attended concert

I was down at Mr Moore's to see J Gibson last night about going to this concert and found him just considering about the same subject; only tickets were the desiderata. He had slipped out from a dinner party of old aunts &c on occasion of his Father's birthday and was only wishing for tickets & a companion to go either to a subscription ball at the Assembly rooms or to the concert. Mr Kerr, who is lodging in the same house with JG had promised his tickets to some ladies but as he did not take them after waiting till almost 9 oclock we took the liberty of making use of them.

The concert was well attended as to numbers the room being crowded. More ladies were present than at the former one. The two overtures I heard ('Zauberflotte' & 'The Miller & his Men') were very well performed. Zauberflotte was encored. Mr Noakes and a basso (I don't know his name) were the only male voices worth listening to – the females were nothing in particular. I was obliged to stand the whole night, but got near and chatted with a Miss Thompson of Higham Place whom Gibson knew a little. She was with a sister and another young lady also two brothers so as there were two gentlemen to three ladies, JG (I unfortunately never having been introduced to them) made the third to set them home and I came away solus.

The concert was advertised in the Newcastle Chronicle 10 March 1827.

VOCAL CONCERT.

MRS GARRICK has the Honour most respectfully to inform the Ladies and Gentlemen of Newcastle and its Vicinity, that, from the Request of many of her musical Friends, she intends giving a Vocal and Instrumental CONCERT on Thursday, March 22d, at the Turk's Head Long Room.

VOCAL PERFORMERS.

Mrs Garrick, Mr Noakes, Mr Stimpson, Mr Brown, Master Peele, and Mr Jones (from the Theatre-Royal).

Leader, Mr Millar. Flute, Mr Richardson.

Mr Monro will preside at the Piano Forte.

Tickets 3s 6d each to be had of Mrs Garrick, 21, Northumberland Street, and at the Music Shops and principal Booksellers.

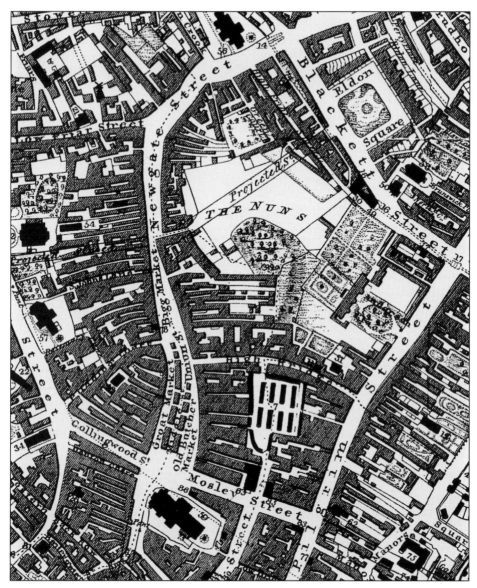

The centre of Newcastle in 1830 showing Newgate Street, where Mr McIntyre originally had his practice, and the newly-built fashionable development of Eldon Square to where he moved his premises in 1829. The Literary & Philosophical Society is lower left, marked 34, opposite Collingwood Street. The old Theatre Royal was on Mosley Street. The map shows Newcastle before Richard Grainger's redevelopment of the town centre swallowed up 'The Nuns' and Anderson Place under Grey Street and Grainger Street during the mid-1830s.

The Theatre Royal

Thomas often writes about going to see plays at the Theatre Royal, which then was the old theatre in Mosley Street, opened in 1788 and demolished when the present Royal was built in 1836. Going to the theatre was a social occasion and a chance to meet people, as well as a night's entertainment. Performances started at 7 and lasted until 11 or later. You could usually get in for half-price after 9 o'clock. Thomas's first visit in January 1827 was a bit of a disappointment.

… on Thursday morning finding I had got pretty near through the accounts having sat up till twelve oclock the night before over them. I made myself a promise that if the accounts were done and the books posted up (I had not made any entries for the new year) by the following night I would treat myself to the Play for the first time this season. 'The Pilot' a new piece was to be the after entertainment so I thought I would only go at half price. Coln & Mrs Gilmore were going (at least their names were in the box book) so I determined on going to the boxes. J Gibson wanted me to go with him so we agreed to go together to half price. Mrs Clementson from Darlington was staying at Shieldfield and I expected would be there as it was fashionable night an extra

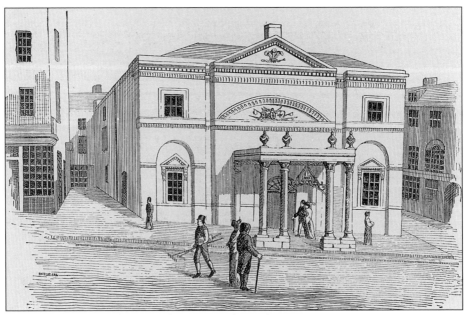

The old Theatre Royal, Mosley Street, c.1820.

inducement to the boxes; and last not least the Miss Gibsons were to go to half play, to see the 'Pilot'. When I was down street in the afternoon I found that the arrangement was altered (by desire) the 'Pilot' the first piece and 'No Song No Supper'. I went to J Gibsons and said we might as well go to full play. As I should meet Coln & Mrs Gilmore &c &c I determined upon going to see all; and accordingly to the boxes we went. To begin my disappointment neither the Coln, his lady, nor any one else I knew were there – the snow I suppose having prevented them and to wind up all I found when I got home (or rather to J Gibsons lodgings) that my watch ribbon had given way and my seals were gone! I made immediate search at the Theatre & told the Watchmen about to look out for them but no tidings have I yet had of them.

Sadly, Thomas never did get his seals back. Later in the 1827 season, a visit of Miss Maria Foote was the attraction.

… I intend to go to the Theatre on Thursday evening to see Miss Foote. I had resolved to go no more this season and have resisted the appearance of two 'stars' but, never having seen Miss F, I cannot resist going to hear and see her … Mr Webb too, the Irish comedian, is to play on Wednesday and Thursday nights along with Miss Foote … A wag says the performers are now Webb-Foote-d!

The playbill for 'The Pilot'.

I was at the Theatre last night and saw the two last acts of 'The Rivals', 'The Weathercock' and the 'Irish Tutor'. Miss Foote neither surprised nor disappointed the expectations I had formed of her. She is certainly beautiful, both in person & figure and her dancing is exquisite. She is a person too who grows more fascinating the longer you look at her. I had never seen 'The Rivals and was glad to see I had formed so just a conception of the characters. Mr A Wright, the Captn Absolute wants power of voice but is otherwise a good actor. I think I should play the character (as well as his other part last night, young Fickle) tolerably, especially to Miss Foote's Lydia Languish. Mr Webb is excellent as Mr Lucius O Trigger. I only went in at half play but passed a very pleasant evening.

Miss Foote, the star attraction, was about 29 when Thomas saw her. She made her debut, aged 12, at Plymouth in 1810 and appeared at Covent Garden in 1814. She was noted for her beauty, although her acting was said to be 'mechanical and lacking spirit'. Nevertheless, while playing in 'The Belle's Stratagem' at Cheltenham, she captivated Colonel Berkeley, who married her when he came into his title of Earl of Harrington in 1831, making her Countess of Harrington.

A holiday in Yorkshire

In September 1827, Thomas had his first holiday since he came back from Edinburgh, and spent it with his mother and father in North Yorkshire. He left Newcastle on Monday, September 10, travelling by gig to Tynemouth, seeing one or two patients on the way. Then he crossed the River Tyne by boat, and took the coach to Sunderland where his parents were living. They set off the next day.

Tuesday 11

Took seats in the Pilot and were set down at Sheraton a village about 5 miles from Hartlepool our intended place of sojourn for a few days. After breakfast Mother and I commenced our walk to the latter place which we greatly prolonged in going round by the sands, – in the end however we arrived safely at the King's Head Inn and found our quarters there very comfortable.

Friday 14

I had yesterday taken places in the Car which runs from Seaton to Stockton and appointed that the vehicle should take Mother & me up at the end of the lane leading from Hartlepool. The car however came past us quite full through negligence of the man whom I had desired to keep places. We walked to Wolviston and after resting there Mother proposed that instead of sending to Stockton for a chaise as was at first intended we should enjoy the afternoon by continuing our walk to Stockton! This I gladly agreed to as I am always a bad traveller inside a closed vehicle. According we got to Stockton towards evening having walked about 14 miles that day altogether.

Saturday 15

Thomas and his mother probably travelled on the Stockton-Darlington Railway, opened in 1825, the world's first public steam railway. Dinsdale Spa near Darlington, also known as Middleton Spa, had a spring discovered in 1789 that was believed to have useful medicinal properties. A bath house and hotel were built there for visitors to the spring in the 1820s

The arrangement was that we were to meet Father this afternoon at or near Neasham. After breakfasting at Stockton the railway coach took us as far as the Fighting Cocks public house from whence we walked through Dinsdale spa to Neasham and not meeting with F proceeded towards Croft to which place

Dinsdale Spa, c.1820

we had just approached when he came up. As no beds were at liberty at Middleton and tolerably comfortable lodgings offered at Neasham it was determined that we should settle there for a few days. At Mrs Gunson's then (dealer in Tea, Coffee, Tobacco and Snuff, with bacon, eggs, and other vegetables!) we unpacked and fixed our quarters.

Tuesday 18

My F had to look after the piano-fortes under his care at Raby Castle and as I had never seen the place I most readily accepted the proposal for me to accompany him … The Castle and grounds were in first rate order as the family were expected in a day or two. The housekeeper ordered lunch for us which I tasted for curiosity sake but we dined at the Queen's Head Inn Staindrop. I was highly gratified with my day's drive and returned to Neasham in the dusk. While my Father was tuning in the different rooms at Raby I had excellent opportunity of seeing all the curiosities by roaming about the apartments. One piano is in Lady Arabella's room and there also she has her private library which I took the liberty of glancing into. Among other volumes was her Ladyship's Album containing many original and pretty pieces.

Lady Arabella was a daughter of the Earl of Darlington, who had his seat at Raby Castle. Thomas's father (also called Thomas Wright) was a well-known musician and music teacher.

Raby Castle, c.1890.

Friday 21

Walked with Mother to Croft; took coach there to Ferryhill near Durham where we staid all night. I was to have come forward to Newcastle that night but my Mother was unwell so I proposed to stay with her till the coaches passed the following afternoon.

Saturday 22

Jumped on to the Express at 5 PM. and arrived in Newcastle about half past 9.

To tea and a dance

Although Thomas's five-year apprenticeship ended at the beginning of April 1829, he continued working as usual until the end of the month. During this time, he received some invitations from his chiefs, Mr McIntyre and Mr Morson, that at least partly recognised his improved status. On Sunday, 12 April, he wrote about one of the parties.

Last night about half past 7 I joined a party of about 30 at Mr Burnup's to tea and a dance, and enjoyed a very agreeable evening. The company consisted of several known faces and some that were new to me. Among the former were besides the Miss Burnups – their cousins Misses Fanny and Ann Burnup, Miss Row, Mr Lang (who was in town for the day and called upon me in the morning) Mr & Mrs Burnup, Messrs Nichol, Richardson, Wm & R Atkinson, Bilton &c; and of the former I only made myself acquainted with Miss Ann Hutton a pretty dark-eyed girl with whom I danced, I believe, four times; her sister Miss Phyllis; Miss Sillick a perfect little mountain whom I durst not engage for a partner through fear of some catastrophe, and who only did get a mate in one or two dances; and Mrs Nichol. Quadrilles, country dances, 'the Coquet' and songs set off the evening till 'past one' when the ladies broke up and I having set Miss AH home made the best of my way back to Eldon Square.

Final dinner parties

And on 20 April:

Mr McIntyre had a state dinner party on Friday at which I was present and the most stylish affair we have had of that kind in the new dining room … Mr McI's dinner was set out in splendid style at 5½ PM and was composed of an abundance of 'bachelor's fare' of which all particularly the wines – Champagne, Claret, Hock, Madeira, Constantia, Clary, white Port (a new wine or rather, I believe, and old one revived), red Port – pronounced to be the very best that need be drunk, – and Sherry, were highly extolled. Dr Morson had an evening music party whither we found the ladies adjourned when we went up to the drawing room but as I was not specially invited I, of course, did not intrude myself nor did the Dr or Mrs M take any notice of my absence by sending out for me.

Dr Morson has invited me to join a dinner party at his table tomorrow though I am only asked to join after dinner, want of room, attention to business &c may be pleaded as an excuse, and we will not stick at trifles considering that when I get there it will be my first appearance in his dining room since the house was inhabited.

The next day he described the occasion.

An agreeable party last night which I joined at 7½ PM and found that there really would not have been room for me at the dinner table. Company present were besides the host, hostess, Miss Jamieson, the partner Mr McI and man Friday Mr Wright; Dr Ross, Mr & Mrs Gouthwaite, Mr (but not Miss) Hedley, Mr Donkin, Mr Jamieson and Mr Winstanly. This last gent: retired early; and after tea two whist tables were formed while the Doctor, Miss J. & I set to work with music; some songs, duets & trios were sung and we finally broke up about 11½ PM. It is justice to say that Dr M chid me for not joining them sooner, and altogether made me feel very much at home during the evening.

After Newcastle

Thomas's last entry in his Diary, on 30 April 1829, was very brief:

All ready to leave in the morning by the Express coach. Mr McIntyre will not sell the horse though F & M most kindly gave me leave for the purchase.

His apprentice days over, Thomas was going home to Croft for a holiday before starting a medical course at London University. He liked Mr McIntyre's horse – the last one he had been riding – and had hoped to buy it from his ex-master at a reasonable price!

So *Diary of a Doctor* ends, but its author does not completely disappear from view just yet ... Thomas used some of the spare pages at the back of his final volume to write brief notes about events in his life between April 1829, when he ended his Diary, and April 1832, when he left England to become a student at the University of Leyden. His notes mention the highlights of his time as a student at London University, where he qualified in 1830 as a Licentiate of Apothecaries Hall (an essential qualification for a doctor at that time) and became a Member of the Royal College of Surgeons in 1831. He also described his student vacations, including the one at Redcar in the summer of 1830 where he met Elizabeth Hubbard (Eliza), who later became his wife.

> 'Miss Hubbard was another Redcar beauty. With the diffidence of a schoolgirl of 16 or 17, she possessed a figure and features that promised in a few years to be highly beautiful. As I gazed on them it seemed as if a Madonna of Titian, or a chef d'ouvre of some master hand was before me in all the loveliness of form and color, but endowed with life; a placid 'harmony of soul and face', and now and then a playful archness – in a year or two this Miss H may become a yet more dangerous associate than her almost namesake 'La Blonde'. On leaving Redcar the Hubbards gave us pressing invitations to visit them in Park Place: I shall not be loath to accept when opportunity offers.'

Although the Diary manuscript tells us about Thomas's life only up to the time he ended his studies at London University, quite a lot is known about his later years from other sources. After studying at Leyden, where he qualified as MD, Thomas returned to England and, in 1833, he settled in Wakefield. There he was appointed as consulting physician to the West Riding Asylum and, over the years, he built a very lucrative private medical practice. Thomas married Elizabeth in 1835 and they had 13 children, only 6 of whom outlived their parents. Elizabeth died in 1890, aged 76, but Thomas lived until 1898, when he was in his 91st year.

Not surprisingly to anyone who has read his Diary, as well as being a successful and well-loved doctor, Thomas Giordani Wright was actively involved in education, science and community work throughout his long life.

*To
The Reader
Who is most gratified by an
attentive Perusal of this
Diary
It is most respectfully
Dedicated
by
The Author.**